Secrets *of* *the* Best-Run Practices

JUDY CAPKO

What Makes Some Practices Stand Out from the Crowd?

GREENBRANCH PUBLISHING

Phoenix, Maryland

Published by Greenbranch Publishing, LLC
PO Box 208
Phoenix, MD 21131
Phone: (800) 933-3711
Fax: (410) 329-1510
Email: info@greenbranch.com
Website: www.mpmnetwork.com, www.soundpractice.net

Printed in the United States of America by United Book Press, Inc. www.unitedbookpress.com

PUBLISHER
Nancy Collins

EDITORIAL ASSISTANT
Jennifer Weiss

BOOK DESIGNER
Laura Carter
Carter Publishing Studio

INDEX
Deborah K. Tourtlotte

COPYEDITOR
Karen Doyle

Dedication

This book is dedicated to Robin and all those great employees that contribute to a medical practice's ultimate success.

TABLE OF CONTENTS

Dedication

Acknowledgements . . . . **viii**

About the Author . . . . **x**

Introduction 1
- The Business of Medicine
- Why this book
- Common threads
- About the book

CHAPTER 1: *The Perfect Receptionist*. 7
- Everyone loves Susan
- The day begins
- Ready, set, go
- Call it what it is
- The secrets

CHAPTER 2: *Conquering Work & Patient Flow Problems* 13
- What was wrong
- The challenge
- The power of data
- The findings
- The remedy
- Searching for a champion
- Making it happen
- Reaping the rewards
- The secrets

CHAPTER 3: *The Amazingly Productive Doctor* 23
- Making time count
- The clinical flow
- Everyone benefits
- Numbers talk
- Lessons learned
- The secrets

CHAPTER 4: *Mastering the Appointment Schedule* **29**
- Looking at the indicators
- Getting to the root of the problem
- The financial impact
- Defining the objectives
- Mastering the schedule
- Checking out the gains
- The secrets

CHAPTER 5: *Commonsense Risk Management*. **41**
- Could it happen to you?
- Start with the relationship
- Documentation
- Develop a risk management plan
- Discharging patients
- Tapping in to risk management resources
- Attitudes
- The secrets

CHAPTER 6: *Team Spirit—Team Power* **53**
- It takes a leader
- Team thinking
- Building from the ground up
- Strengthening the team
- Sharing goals
- Team spirit
- The power of the team
- The secrets

CHAPTER 7: *The Dynamics of the Outpatient Academic Practice* **61**
- Competing priorities
- A world of difference
- Administrative challenges
- Operational assessment
- Clinic performance
- Customer service
- Building trust
- Facing change
- Taking action
- The secrets

CHAPTER 8: *The Power of Revenue Management* 75
- Capturing charges
- Charge reporting
- Revenue recovery
- Monitoring performance
- Accounts receivable management
- Whose practice is it anyway?
- The embezzler
- The secrets

CHAPTER 9: *Great Employees—The Simple Truth* 95
- Look at Robin
- Get off to a good start
- The visible manager
- Open communication
- Make everyone a winner
- No-tolerance policy
- Your #1 customer
- The secrets

CHAPTER 10: *The Money Crunch* 111
- They grew too fast
- Checking out the numbers
- The infrastructure
- The final diagnosis
- No pain, no gain
- Turnaround strategies
- The action plan
- The results
- The next step
- The secrets

CHAPTER 11: *Reshaping the Practice—A New Genre* 125
- What do you want to do?
- Doing it right
- Making it happen
- The boutique practice
- Shifting to cosmetics
- Going bariatrics
- Other opportunities
- In the end

CHAPTER 12: *The Practice of The Future* **139**
- The Quality Factor
- Focus on Employees
- Advancing Technology
- One step at at time

Toolbox **147**

Index **173**

Acknowledgements

A special thanks to my husband, Joe, who provided the inspiration and encouragement for this book. He is always ready to listen and endured my countless hours of pounding away at the keyboard and burning the midnight oil. Joe has supported my career moves with enthusiasm and was instrumental in my decision to become a consultant more than 20 years ago. He has always believed in me, and he gave me endless encouragement during those early, occasionally difficult times. I am forever grateful.

A big thank you goes to Nancy Collins, the publisher, for her confidence in me. She is a dream to work with; always considerate, flexible and understanding. Thanks to all the Greenbranch staff that contributed to this book becoming a reality, including: Karen Doyle for providing invaluable support in editing the manuscript and making sure it was completely understandable to the reader; Jennifer Weiss for her editorial assistance and Deborah Tourtlotte for indexing the book. Also, Laura Carter of Carter Publishing Studio did a fantastic job with both the book interior design and its cover.

Thanks to my son Joe Capko Jr., and my good friends and colleagues Rebecca Anwar, Mary Jean Sage and Linda Williams who read and critiqued different chapters of the manuscript before they were submitted to the publisher. I am also thankful to those kind physicians and practice administrators that agreed to review prepublished chapters of the book in preparation for its release.

Of course, this book would never have been written if it weren't for the many physicians that sought my services and opened the door to "secrets of the best run practices." I thank each of you. Because of time constraints, I was unable to obtain permission from all of the practices featured in this book. Therefore, the anonymity of some of the practices has been protected through use of fictitious names and locations.

I offer many thanks to those physicians and their staff that are mentioned by their actual names in the book. Not only did they consent to being featured in the book, but each one also graciously granted me one more interview as I prepared the manuscript. It is my pleasure to showcase these very special practices.

I would be remiss if I failed to honor my incredible mother, Mildred Bentz. Growing up, she always encouraged me to step out of my comfort zone and follow my dreams. I can still hear her telling me, "nothing ventured, nothing gained." Thank you Mom—you were right.

Above all, my thanks to an awesome God, for he makes all things possible.

About the Author

Judy Capko is the founder of Capko & Company, www.capko.com. Judy has specialized in medical practice operations and marketing for more than 20 years and is a certified risk management specialist. Her emphasis is on building patient-centered strategies and valuing staff's contribution. Beyond this, she focuses on maximizing resources, resulting in improved operational and financial performance. Hundreds of physicians and administrators have benefited from her advice and innovative, energetic approach to organizational management and strategic planning. Judy has gained national recognition in her field, working with both small and large practices, as well as major academic faculty practices from coast to coast. She was a charter member of the National Association of Health Care Consultants and the past marketing chairperson for the Society of Medical-Dental Management Consultants. Judy served on the advisory panel and was a frequent presenter for Quality Forums, a national program sponsored by Pfizer Pharmaceutical. She judged the national "Physician of the Year" competition, sponsored by Physicians Practice, Inc., in 2001 and 2002.

Judy is a popular speaker for major health care conferences, national specialty associations, health care systems, regional medical societies and health care executive summits. She has been interviewed by and authored hundreds of articles for over 30 prestigious national medical journals including *American Medical News, Family Practice Management, Group Practice Journal, The Journal of Medical Practice Management, Medical Economics, Ophthalmology Times, Orthopedics Today, Physicians Advisory,* and *Physicians Practice.*

Introduction

In my 20-some years as a practice management consultant, I have worked with hundreds of practices reaching out for help. Some were in troubled waters and about to sink. Others needed only a few navigational tools to get them back on course. When a practice pulls together, it can move into calm waters and set a new course for its destination. With the demands of running a busy practice in the 21st century, this isn't easy.

Seeking help in building the proverbial better mousetrap contributes to a manager's success. Some managers are driven by a desire to be the best. After all, there's a lot of industry hype these days about "best practices." But what does it take to really be the best, and what are the best practices?

The definition of best, according to the *New World Dictionary* is: "The most excellent sort; surpassing all others, most desirable, most favorable and most profitable." It's a lofty goal to be the best. Many seek it, few achieve it. There's one thing you can count on—even the best can't be the best at everything.

This book will help you on your journey, featuring information about practices that have mastered particular areas of operation, ultimately improving business performance. It covers everything from how to manage phone calls to staying on schedule; from meeting patient demands to improving patient satisfaction; and from risk management to taking charge of the revenue cycle and improving practice finances. The book is intended to provide you with insight and tips to help you improve various aspects of practice performance, in a way that is thought provoking and perhaps a call to action.

THE BUSINESS OF MEDICINE

Practicing medicine and running your practice like a business have never been more challenging. The environment in which we do business focuses on protecting patients' rights, developing legal requirements for physicians, offering the best clinical care available and managing the health care dollar. At the same time, everyone involved is supposed to take pride in his or her job, enjoy the work and provide red carpet service. That's a tall order by any stretch of the imagination.

Eroding profits and the emphasis on quality are primary reasons that medical practices seek ways to reduce processes and improve efficiency. It is essential for everyone in the practice to accomplish as much as possible in a day. Managers focus on ways to keep staff motivated and productive and patients happy.

Most of us discover, along the way, that there is much to gain through sharing the experiences and lessons learned of other medical practices. Our peers give us insight, enabling us to achieve greater gains. Running a medical practice should be, and can be, exciting and rewarding.

WHY THIS BOOK?

Everyone loves a good story, one that has a few surprises, gets our juices flowing and leaves us feeling good. If we find the story intriguing and it reveals a few secrets, so much the better. This is true whether it relates to our personal life or the work we do. This book is about the business of medicine and secrets learned along the way.

I'll highlight success stories from practices much like yours and answer questions so often asked: "How do other practices do this?" "What do you see in other practices?" "Is there a better way to do it?" and "What should we do?" *Secrets of the Best-Run Practices* will answer these questions and showcase the best. It shares experiences and opinions on what it takes to be among the best. These secrets can often be applied to the practice as basic standards to help it become one of the "best run" practices.

In over 10 years working in medical practices and managing offices, followed by 20 years of consulting, I have been privileged to work with hundreds of practices with a wide variety of specialties and sizes, each with its own set of problems to be solved and goals to be achieved. I've traveled many paths, none of them the same.

Different types of practices have different needs. In large, prestigious academic centers, physicians have the demands of teaching, research and seeing their clinic patients. These contrasting demands sometimes cause conflict. The needs of the clinic often become a shifting priority. But in the end, these doctors and administrators want to make sure the patients' needs are met and that the clinic is run efficiently, much the same as their counterparts in solo or group private practice.

Another common scenario involves Dr. New, excited about finishing his residency and opening a new practice. He is often overwhelmed at the regulatory and financial requirements it takes to get a practice up and running. He is not prepared for the endless paperwork and the decisions that must be made: everything from how the practice is structured to where it will be located, to how it will be equipped and how it will be staffed. He needs a carefully crafted business plan and timeline to guide him.

Then there are practices that have been so successful they aren't prepared to handle their unexpected growth. The infrastructure is not sufficient to handle the rapid increase in volume. This can result in chaos, unhappy patients, an inability to stay on top of the workload and a slow down in cash flow. Their needs become emergent.

On the opposite side of the spectrum, there is the young practice with an eager doctor that is equally frustrated by the gaps in her appointment schedule and the time it takes to build a solid practice and meet her financial commitments. This requires patience and a marketing plan to grow the business.

No two practices are alike. They face varying demands and challenges. Some demands can be anticipated—but there are surprises that simply result from the ever-changing business of running a practice. Demands from industry and government are continually changing, and new political problems emerge. Practices face economic challenges such as lower reimbursement and the malpractice crisis. There are uninsured and underinsured patients. There are problems running an urban practice and other problems associated with rural health clinics. An emerging workforce with different values and expectations, along with a more demanding consumer, add to the complexity of running a practice. Changing and varying demands effect how a practice is managed and what is required of managers. It influences what goals they want to set, what they need to accomplish those goals and what it takes to be a top performer.

COMMON THREADS

Best run practices have many similarities that contribute to their success. These common threads begin with the people that guide the practice. They know who they are, where they want to go and what it takes to get there. There are six distinctive traits found in those that are at the helm of outstanding practices, and these traits contribute to their ability to set a course, guide the crew and reach their destination.

1. **Lead and they will follow.** The leaders of best run practices encourage people to achieve their best. They recognize the strengths of each individual and build upon them, unlocking each employee's potential. Above all they listen—I mean *really* listen, to the staff. They listen to their ideas. When it is possible, they will use those ideas to help them build a better run practice. They listen to their needs and concerns, and provide guidance and support.

2. **It's the people.** For every ship there is a captain, but the ship never leaves the dock without a crew. The best physician leaders, administrators, managers and supervisors know that. They believe in and understand the value of staff. Simply stated, they depend on staff members and have faith in their capabilities, motivating them to do their best. They involve the staff in setting goals and communicate clearly. They get everyone on board; and when the objectives are reached, together they celebrate their successes. In other words, they share the glory. It is the collective team that makes the practice!

3. **Invest in the practice.** No matter how tight revenue is and how difficult it is to manage expenses, the best run practice is not afraid to spend money—wisely. Management supports staff growth and job enrichment. In best run practices, funds are set aside for continuing education at every level. Employees are paid well, trained properly and given the tools they need to do a better job. These practices understand return on investment: exploring opportunities to improve the facility, upgrade equipment and integrate new technology.

4. **Manage things.** The best leaders manage things, not people. They set standards and put systems in place. They gather and manage data to monitor the practice's performance, examine trends and reward those that excel. They make data-driven decisions that keep the practice on course.

5. **Look to the future.** Forward thinking practices outshine their peers in most aspects. They have administrators and physicians that always see a light at the end of the tunnel. These practices don't live in the past, they live in the now, and they look to the future. They explore change openly and grasp new technology. They are continually learning and challenging their own knowledge base, thinking "out of the box." They listen, they participate and they make change happen for the greater good.

6. **Back to basics.** As much as the best run practices look to the future and remain progressive, they also focus on and respect the basics. They

work to keep their practices uncomplicated and their patients happy. They are quick to focus on the basics of quality; getting it right the first time, eliminating unnecessary steps, communicating well and respecting people, time and resources.

These common threads are distinct from each other, but each plays a role in achieving overall excellence. Together, these elements distinguish top leaders and their ability to inspire high performance, mutual respect, pride in accomplishments and a desire to share the glory.

So what happens when the administrator or physician manager doesn't possess all of these leadership traits? It doesn't mean the practice is in troubled waters, and it certainly doesn't diminish the skills that contribute to the success already achieved. This list of traits can be used as a self-evaluation tool, giving managers an opportunity to assess their management style.

Managers continually mold their leadership skills—there is no perfect leader. Those that excel are always seeking ways to enhance their talents. Throughout their career, they redefine who they are and how they adapt to a changing marketplace. It's a humbling experience. What are the principles and values that guide those at the helm of the practice? What secrets can be learned from other practices, and what driving forces will be integral in your search to be the best?

ABOUT THE BOOK

Not enough time, not enough money, and too many demands. This is the dilemma of medical practices as they struggle with the kaleidoscope of complex problems involved with managing a busy medical practice. *Secrets of the Best-Run Practices* provides the inside scoop on how some physicians and administrators faced with these challenges improved critical aspects of the practice's performance.

By reading this book, you will find out what makes some medical practices stand out from the crowd, as it highlights practices that just seem to have that special touch. For instance, Chapter 1, The Perfect Receptionist, will introduce you to a star receptionist who performs her job with ease and confidence. She makes every patient *feel* special, and she understands how important her job is. Chapter 3 features a physician that has it wired when it comes to maximizing his productivity, outperforming his peers around the country.

Commonsense Risk Management (Chapter 5) emphasizes the importance of structuring a program to reduce risk within the practice and details how a little more attention to your patients can provide more than an ounce of prevention. Also featured in this book in Chapter 6 is the astute administrator that empowered physicians and staff, creating a team whose performance marks are bound to impress most of you.

Chapter 7 spotlights the challenges of the academic practice and how it differs from the traditional community practice. But as you will see, in the end, it is essential for this type of practice to resolve business challenges and deal with customer service issues.

The steps required to better manage revenue and improve financial results are reviewed in Chapter 8, which provides tips on how to maximize charge capture and revenue-recovery strategies to improve collection. There is also a segment on how to protect the practice from the embezzler.

The book goes on to share the secret of what it takes to makes good employees great! Chapter 9 is loaded with solid, practical advice on obtaining peak performance from your employees. The Money Crunch (Chapter 10) tells a tale of woe about a practice that grew too fast and almost imploded. You will learn how this happened and the steps that were essential for recovery from this debacle.

Reshaping the Practice—a New Genre (Chapter 11) describes three different practices at a crossroads and what they did to change their destiny. The final chapter, The Practice of the Future, provides my spin on what will continue to be the focus of leading medical practices, as they apply technology to their advantage and seek innovative approaches to serving both their patients and their staff.

The book also highlights some less-than-perfect practices that have made painful mistakes, but overcame them with a no-nonsense approach that you can apply to your practice if faced with a similar situation. Some of the case studies may seem familiar and be a reminder of past challenges and obstacles you overcame. For example, dealing with workflow problems that wreak havoc and cause frustration, or scheduling demands that compromise efficiency and patient service.

The toolbox at the back of the book is an added bonus. It is packed with sample forms and tools used in the featured best run practices. These practical tools can be adapted for use in your own practice.

This book highlights only a few practices, but it is a helpful reminder that while problems are a challenge, solutions are always just around the corner. The trick is getting everyone on the same page. Read on and enjoy!

CHAPTER 1

The Perfect Receptionist

Most offices have done away with the sliding glass window that separated staff from patients entering the office, but many still have a long way to go before they excel with customer service at the front desk. As a Mystery Patient, hired to evaluate the patient encounter, I've seen it all.

> **KEY FACT:** *Recognize the role of the receptionist as a powerful position, and give it the attention (and respect) it deserves.*

I have discovered that it is a rarity for a receptionist to actually introduce herself or welcome patients to the practice. I recall a number of offices where the sign-in sheet seemed to be a tool that gave the receptionist permission to eliminate a personal greeting and give no attention to the patient's arrival. I remember a time when I arrived at the check-in counter and observed three staff members chatting in the background, refusing to make eye contact with me. I can only assume that as long as they pretended I wasn't there, I didn't exist. No one assumed responsibility for helping me. You can imagine how this makes a patient feel.

In another office, there wasn't an employee to be seen when I arrived at the reception counter. After I had waited more than five minutes, someone appeared and acted rather nonchalant. And I recall other times when I stood at a counter while the receptionist was on a personal phone call. She wasn't about to let my presence interfere. I wasn't terribly excited to listen in on a conversation between her and her boyfriend, discussing their Saturday night escapade. Then there were those countless times when there was a receptionist with an attitude—a bad attitude!

More often than not, I can tell within a minute if the receptionist has an attitude, or whether she likes her job and is glad that I'm there—she just can't hide it. There are receptionists that are perfunctory and do exactly what is required of them. They ask only pertinent questions and seem anxious to complete their transaction with me. Oh yes, and then there are those disgruntled and harried employees, each one obviously unhappy and annoyed at my presence. How dare I interrupt her!

The novice is another story. He wants to help, but just doesn't have a clue about what to do and can't answer basic questions. When the person greeting you lacks competence, the patient's confidence in the practice instantly diminishes. This is cause for concern.

Some receptionists just don't want to be bothered, shooting a blank "I don't know" stare with the first question they are asked, refusing to take responsibility.

Considering the receptionist is usually the first person a patient meets, it doesn't say much for the practice's curb appeal if the patient's experiences are anything like those just described. However, there are practices, although few and far between, with a star receptionist that is the perfect greeter.

EVERYONE LOVES SUSAN

We all welcome the rare receptionist—the one that just loves her job and shows it. She's sensational. I know her, and her name is Susan. Everyone loves Susan. She smiles; she's energetic; she's happy to see you; and she, most obviously, loves her job. Everyone loves Susan because she makes them feel important, and she's a joy to be around.

Why is Susan such a joy to be around? It's not because the work is easy. Susan works for a busy four-physician dermatology practice. She greets and registers more than 100 patients a day. It's not because she calls the shots and does only what she wants. It's because Susan has an important job and has been given the tools to do it right. It's because she knows what her tasks are and what is expected of her. She takes pride in her job and what she accomplishes. Susan has a lot to do, and she gets it done.

THE DAY BEGINS

Because the role of receptionist varies incredibly from practice to practice and often requires a jack-of-all-trades, I observed Susan at work and was impressed from beginning to end. She knows the secrets to being a great receptionist.

It starts with the morning huddle. At the beginning of each day, Susan meets with the doctors and the nurses that will be handling the day's clinic sessions. Together, they review the schedule and discuss any problems they might anticipate and how each person should handle the situation. For example, if the 3 o'clock patient does not speak English, Susan will need to find out if an English-speaking friend or family member will be accompanying her. Or, there might be an elderly patient that will need assistance undressing and may take longer then expected. Susan could be asked to juggle the schedule a little if it helps avoid an anticipated delay.

On a separate note, morning huddles are a wonderful way for practices to get a handle on their day. It's an organizational aid to help plan the day, perceive needs and develop interceptive strategies to avoid potential problems. Many practices use this as an opportunity to review the prior day's activities as well. Usually, this planning and communication tool takes less then five minutes a day and gets you off to a great start.

READY, SET, GO

Now Susan is ready to run with the ball, and her priority is the patients. Despite the high volume of activity, she is calm, confident and eager to please. Her first role is to greet and assist the patients, answering whatever questions they may have. Unlike many receptionists, Susan is not responsible for taking incoming phone calls or scheduling telephone appointments. Without these interruptions, she can focus on the patients and give them the attention they deserve. The responsibility of registering new patients, updating demographics on the computer system and scanning each patient's insurance card is done with ease.

Susan knows what needs to be done. If the patient is scheduled for services that are not covered by insurance, she calls the patient aside and (quietly) reminds him or her of the estimated charges to be paid for those services, as well as any other co-pay due at the end of the visit. She then instant messages this conversation to the exit station. This lets the check-out receptionist know that the patient has been informed and is prepared to pay.

Now that the patient is ready to be seen, she generates a charge ticket, but isn't required to handle it or the chart. The charge ticket is printed at the nurse's station, where the day's charts are stored, providing the nurse with a nonverbal signal of the patient's arrival. Susan is uninterrupted and has not abandoned her desk, enabling her to move on to serve other arriving patients and guests.

Susan uses e-communication to her advantage. If there is something Susan wants the nurse or doctor to know about the patient she checked in, she will send an instant message to their computer. For example: Mrs. Smith must be seen quickly, she has to be at the ophthalmologist at 3 o'clock. There may be a more personal message: Handle Mr. Wells with kid gloves. He is upset because he was pulled over by a police officer on his way to the office. This keeps the staff well informed of what to expect, is accomplished at Susan's convenience and allows her to remain at her workstation.

Patient activity is monitored throughout the day. Susan keeps an eye on the schedule and tracks how long patients have been waiting in the reception room. If there are delays, she checks her computer to see if a nurse has sent an instant message, explaining the delay and predicting when the patient will be taken to an examining room. Susan then gives the patient her attention, explains the situation and offers an apology. She asks if there is anything else she can do to make the patient more comfortable.

These processes eliminate many steps and improve communication for the typical receptionist. Susan is able to greet and check-in an established patient in less than two minutes. Her average time with a new patient is less than five minutes. Interruptions are minimized; she isn't handling paperwork unnecessarily and is not abandoning her station. She uses her computer to do the walking and the talking.

When she is updating the patient's account, Susan can pull up notes that guide her to engage in enough small talk to make the patient feel incredibly important. For example, "Angela, how's the new job going?" or "Mr. Jones, how was your trip to Hawaii?" She focuses entirely on each patient and does it with ease.

By the way, when Susan greets a new patient she always welcomes him or her to the practice and introduces herself. Susan wears a nametag so each person will always remember who they spoke with. She ends each encounter with the patient by asking, *"Is there anything else I can do for you?"*

When Susan is not assisting a patient or other visitor, she will check her interoffice e-mail, confirm appointments, open and sort the mail and prepare both the new-patient welcome kits and thank you notes to the people that have referred patients. All this can be done at her station, in her own time, and never interferes with her helping a patient. The work comes to her. Other than her breaks, the only time she leaves her station is to tidy up the reception area.

Susan's workload is manageable, but the volume is monitored on a regular basis. The office manager tracks the number of patients each day, separating new and established patients. The variables in patient type, by age and insurance, are reviewed, as they impact how much time Susan spends with patients. Changes are made quickly should demands on the receptionist's time change. Support for a skilled receptionist is one of the most immediate ways the practice demonstrates its commitment to patients.

CALL IT WHAT IT IS

Call the position what it is—the receptionist! When I asked Susan to describe her job she said, "I'm the receptionist. My job is important and pivotal to the practice's success. I am the first person to greet patients and make them comfortable. It's my job to gather accurate information to expedite the patient visit, keep the patient happy and ensure that we get paid for what we do." She went on to say, "I love my job. Everyone depends on me." She is right—and she is the perfect receptionist!

The Secrets

1. Recognize the importance of the receptionist and skills required to do the job right!
2. Simplify and clarify the position.
3. Let the computer do the talking and the walking.
4. Assign tasks that support reduced interruptions.
5. In high volume practices the receptionist should not serve as the primary source for incoming phone calls or scheduling patients.
6. Let the work come to the receptionist.
7. Monitor workload volume and demands.
8. Staff appropriately to meet patient needs.

FORMS ADDED TO YOUR TOOLBOX:

☞ *Sample job description:* Receptionist (p. 148)

Conquering Workflow Problems

"We need help. Our receptionists are drowning, and the patients are outraged," pleaded Mark Schroeder, the administrator of a six-physician orthopaedic practice in the Midwest. In this practice, some of the biggest problems centered on patients arriving at the office. For starters, it was taking too long to check patients in and out. The physicians were getting behind schedule, which wreaked havoc during the clinic sessions. The patients were disgruntled with the long delays. The receptionists didn't have time to verify patient demographics, and they certainly weren't going to ask already angry patients for money. The receptionists and nurses never felt "caught up," and they were frustrated. So were the doctors. The problems were maddening for everyone, and emotions were running high.

On my initial visit to the practice, I saw the problems first hand. Four doctors were scheduled to see patients, and there were four lines of patients waiting to check in. As I approached the desk, I discovered each of the four receptionists was wearing a headset, making it impossible for patients to know if the receptionist was on the phone or prepared to assist them. The check-in process was moving at a snail's pace.

WHAT WAS WRONG

Each of the six physicians had his own check-in station, managed by his receptionist. Most of the physicians felt "their" receptionist was the only one that knew their patients, understood what was needed and had the skills to properly manage the appointment schedule. Therefore, their receptionist was the only one trusted to check in patients, schedule telephone appointments, check out patients and schedule follow-up appointments. Nonetheless, the current system was failing both patients and staff.

The receptionists could not give patients the attention they needed and deserved. Each receptionist had a choice: either ignore callers by placing them on hold or letting them drop into the voice mailbox, or ignore the patient checking-in to deal with callers and schedule their appointments.

When phone calls dropped to voice mail, they would linger there for hours before the receptionists found time to retrieve them. Patients calling for appointments would hang up in frustration or leave curt messages, and were forced to keep calling back. The incoming calls were multiplying like rabbits in spring, and patient satisfaction was plummeting.

A patient bottleneck at checkout was aggravated by what was happening back in the clinic. Patients that had already seen the doctor stood waiting for the nurse who was wrestling with paperwork or talking on the phone. These patients were delayed because nurses were taking clinical calls from other patients, insurance carriers and other physicians. In between these calls, the nurses would be calling other diagnostic centers to schedule their doctor's patients. They were bogged down with phone calls and paperwork that hampered patient flow—keeping patients longer in the back office and slowing their move to the checkout counter. As if this wasn't enough, the nurses were even completing disability forms and dealing with workers' compensation adjusters.

The practice habitually ran late with anxious patients waiting for their turn. No wonder staff turnover was rampant and disgruntled patients were speaking out.

THE CHALLENGE

I had seen similar situations before. Too many people were doing the same thing! By centralizing some of these tasks, efficiency, workflow and patient service would improve dramatically. The first step would be to gather data to clarify how serious the problem was and identify underlying factors. Collecting the data would be time consuming, but not difficult. The biggest challenge I anticipated was convincing the physicians to change a system they were comfortable with.

Mark and I both knew getting the physicians to approve a change would take nothing short of a miracle. These orthopaedic surgeons had the "my girl" syndrome. They couldn't imagine anyone but their own nurse and receptionist helping them or their patients. Convincing them to centralize would be a hard sell. So we began building our case.

THE POWER OF DATA

Data talk—they are tangible evidence that helps define problems, predict results and influence the decision-making process. Data should be the foundation for planning and negotiation. Before we could get physician buy-in to change the ways things were being done, we needed data that would describe the extent of the problem and the value of redistributing the work more efficiently.

A committee composed of a receptionist, a nurse and the clinical supervisor, headed by the practice administrator, assisted with the project. This core group would be invaluable in convincing staff and doctors of the need for change. The committee met to discuss the extent of the problem and the best way to collect sound data.

First we turned to the systems. A report on the number of new and established patients seen in the office was pulled from the computer's practice management system. The scheduling system's templates showed us the appointment slots reserved for the various appointment types for each physician.

The telephone system generated a report providing call information for every telephone: how many total calls were coming in, how long each call took and how many calls were abandoned. But the report didn't tell us the nature of the calls. So we conducted a study, timing the length it took to schedule 10 separate new-patient appointments and 10 separate established-patient appointments uninterrupted. We also documented how often the receptionists were on the telephone when a patient arrived.

The nurses and receptionists were called on to help us collect data from each point of service—the "moments of truth." These detailed data about the types and volume of various activities allowed for a comprehensive view of the overall workflow problems: The data collected included:
- Number of incoming appointment calls, separating new and established patients;
- Average time for a nurse to complete a patient visit if uninterrupted;
- Number of phone calls dropping to voice mail for the receptionists and nurses; and
- The number of abandoned calls.

Each receptionist was enlisted to document the volume of appointment telephone calls received over a one-week period, including those that dropped into voice mail. Most of the receptionists saw the light at the end of the tunnel and were more than willing to lend a helping hand. They knew we were there to make their job easier.

The information collected would enable us to calculate the volume of calls, determine peak hours and examine the various call patterns for each physician. We anticipated and observed variations based on their individual practice style and patient mix. One problem we discovered was the barrage of calls when staff returned from lunch. The practice shut down the phones during lunch break—at the most convenient time for many patients to call for appointments.

The next step depended on the nurses. A patient visit time study was essential to understand workflow throughout the patient visit. We needed to know how much time was lost during a patient visit and why.

Each receptionist and nurse tracked visits for their physician for three days. A patient visit time study form was placed on the chart of every third patient. Exact time was documented on the form as the patient flowed through each process, from check-in to checkout. This gave us solid information on the cause and effect of existing workflow processes.

Additional data were gathered through interviews and observing this busy orthopaedic practice for several days. The observations were very telling—frustrations mounted through the day, and a series of various types of interruptions and activities hampered workflow and consumed time for nurses and receptionists.

THE FINDINGS

Armed with these data, the analysis began. The investigation provided both predictable and startling results. The demand was pinpointed, and workflow processes were clarified:

- The receptionists each handled an average of 39 incoming appointment calls a day, with a low of 22 and high of 56 on a single day. When tracking time, those that dropped to voice mail (VM) required an additional 1.5 minutes to retrieve the message and return the call:
  - 33 established patients:
    - Direct: 20 at 3 minutes each
    - VM: 13 @ 4.5 minutes each

- 6 new patients:
  - — Direct: 4 at 8 minutes each
  - — VM: 2 at 9.5 minutes each
- Sixty-five percent of the telephone requests for appointments occurred between the hours of 9:00 AM and noon.
- Abandoned calls spiked between 12:15 PM and 2:00 PM, accounting for 37% of the total calls received during this time.
- Monday and Friday mornings reported the highest call volume.
- Eighty percent of the patients arrived within five minutes of their scheduled appointment.
- Check-in for an established patient was taking an average of six minutes.
- New patient check-in required 9.5 minutes.
- The receptionist was free from the phones to greet patients on arrival only 25% of the time.
- Patients were roomed as early as five minutes or as long as 52 minutes following completion of the check-in process. On average, the delay was 26 minutes.
- The peak times for bottlenecks in the front office were directly related to the peak time for incoming phone calls and were most severe between 10:30 AM and noon, and again between 2:00 PM and 2:30 PM.
- The peak times for bottlenecks in the clinical setting were in the late morning and again around 4:30 PM.
- Physicians arrived in the exam room an average of 33 minutes after the appointment time for established patients and 39 minutes for new patients.
- The time to schedule outside studies delayed patient checkout by five minutes, but created a secondary delay as the nurse was detained from rooming another patient.
- The time span between conclusion of the doctor's visit and completing in-house studies was 45 minutes. Many times, patients were held up in the sub-wait station, as staff conducting the diagnostic studies got backed-up.
- Scheduling templates showed that often two or three physicians would be seeing new patients at the same time, creating a backlog with x-ray and ultrasound.
- When patients came out of the exam room, one out of three waited for assistance in scheduling studies while the nurse finished a phone call.

- Each nurse had a daily average of nine calls from workers' compensation insurance adjusters.
- Each nurse scheduled an average of 11 outpatient diagnostic studies each day, 8 of these requiring pre-authorization.
- On average, 18 patients were seen for each morning session and 21 for each afternoon session. This meant each receptionist was checking-in and -out an average of 39 patients, and 6 of these were new.
- The patient checkout process averaged 6.5 minutes.

Our investigation indicated that it would require two full-time schedulers to manage the volume of telephone appointments once dedicated schedulers were in place. We also thought that the practice's website should be enhanced so that new patients could pre-register online, and a number of existing patients could schedule their own appointments. These website enhancements would considerably reduce the call volume for the schedulers.

Because they would be relieved of telephone scheduling, the receptionists would have an additional 2½ hours a day to dedicate to receiving and processing patients during clinic sessions. This added time would allow them to adequately review patient demographics and update insurance information. On the checkout side, training would be provided on collecting over-the-counter (OTC) payments, both co-pays and outstanding patient balances.

Preventing multiple physicians from seeing new patients at the same time would level out the demands on in-house diagnostic studies and help improve patient flow in the clinic. Combined with freeing nurses from clerical tasks, this would keep the sessions moving and open up additional time. Nurses could then be assigned the responsibility of auditing each patient's charge ticket to ensure no charges were dropped and diagnoses were recorded.

THE REMEDY

With data in hand, the solutions were clear. If the workload was redistributed through task-related centralization, the majority of the existing flow problems could be solved. The receptionists and nurses could now ensure charges were captured, payments were made and demographics were updated. With proper training and clear expectations, greater efficiency and profitability could be expected.

1. The preliminary action plan was crafted:

1. Remove telephone scheduling from the front desk receptionists and centralize.
   a. Assign two receptionists to be full-time schedulers and relocate them to a quiet location.
   b. The four remaining receptionists would be responsible for each of the six physicians when they were in session. This would not be difficult as there were never more than four physicians in session simultaneously, and 50% of the time only three physicians were in session at one time.
2. Provide telephone coverage during the lunch hours.
3. Eliminate nurses obtaining insurance authorization and scheduling outside diagnostic studies.
   a. When the fourth receptionist was not in sessions, she would obtain insurance authorizations and schedule all the outside diagnostic studies that had been ordered.
4. Remove clerical duties from nursing by reassigning completion of disability and workers' compensation return-to-work forms to medical records staff. Begin research on the potential to automate these processes
5. Train staff appropriately for the new tasks to be assumed.
6. Establish daily collection goals for OTC payments.
7. Change the physician scheduling templates to stagger new-patient visits.

Because his nurse was near and dear to each physician's heart, getting the support for change would be more than a little difficult. However, support from the top was essential. The key was getting one physician to endorse the new workflow model and change in staffing responsibilities. Past experience predicted that if we succeeded with converting one physician, a commitment from the other physicians would soon follow.

SEARCHING FOR A CHAMPION

Our first charge was to identify the doctor that would champion our cause and be willing to lead the pack. One physician, Arthur James, M.D., stood out. He was the most forward thinking and decisive of the group. He was also influential with the other physicians. At a meeting to present the data to the remaining physicians and solicit their support, Dr. James played a key role in gaining their confidence and impressing them with the expected gains that could be achieved. He was a master at overcoming objectives and obtaining consensus.

When the evidence was laid out and the plan was presented, the doctors quickly saw the advantages. They knew there was a solid rationale behind our recommendations, but still feared an overall loss of control. Mark and I explained that they could set up their own protocols for scheduling. The doctors could also have input as we developed the training modules for scheduling. A meeting with each physician and the scheduler would take place before the switch was made, and the transition would be unhurried and methodical. Morning huddles with involved staff would begin as soon as the program was launched. Regular meetings would be scheduled during the first 90 days to make sure each physician's needs were being met and problems were quickly solved. Convinced the plan was sound, the doctors approved our plan, and we put it in motion.

MAKING IT HAPPEN

The committee had a lot of planning to accomplish before the transition could begin. The schedulers were added to our committee to solidify their commitment, help us finalize the plan and assist with a smooth transition.

The pre-launch planning took on a life of its own. I headed this effort with the assistance of the administrator and the support of the planning committee. There were planning meetings and interviews. Flow charts and training guides were developed. Job descriptions were revised and implemented. There were telephone scripts, practice sessions and more meetings. We anticipated some resistance, but with the support of their peers that served on the committee, most of the employees accepted our plan with little resistance.

A system was developed to monitor the number and length of telephone calls and to measure the scheduling demands against the capacity of the two schedulers. We needed to follow our progress, know the staffing needs and make any necessary adjustments.

At last, the detailed action plan was ready for implementation. Because the committee members had been actively involved in the development of the model, they were enthusiastic and influential in bringing the remaining staff on board. It didn't take much for staff to visualize how the new workflow model would improve their life on the job—creating a better work environment and manageable workload. The crowning glory would be an end to disgruntled patients. They were about to see all this become a reality!

There were some adjustments that needed to be made during the first few weeks and quite a bit of handholding. There were morning huddles with physicians, receptionists, nurses and schedulers, during which time they would discuss any issues from the previous day, review the daily schedule and prepare for any potential problems that might emerge. At the end of two weeks, the physicians and staff members involved in the process met with the committee to review their progress and discuss any suggested modifications to the plan. In general, everything was on track and moving forward.

REAPING THE REWARDS

Within 60 days of launching the new workflow model, staff and physicians were touting its success. Patients were roomed on time, and the work was flowing. There was no grumbling from patients or staff. Communication was greatly improved. There were fewer interruptions and no disruption! The real bonus was getting out of the office on time. One would be hard pressed to argue with this type of success.

When it comes to patient care and related workflow, this practice is ticking like a fine Swiss clock. The fog of confusion and chaos has disappeared, replaced by a streamlined system that is seamless in meeting the needs of physicians, staff and patients.

The receptionists' productivity has skyrocketed. They now have time to put new-patient demographics in the computer and update changes for existing patients. The benefits are seen in the insurance department, as rejected claims have diminished, improving cash flow. At the same time, cash flow has been given an additional boost because the receptionists now have time to collect OTC payments from patients. In fact, OTC payments increased by 100% within six months.

The nurses are able to assist their patients as they come out of the exam room. Paperwork is processed quicker, and patient care is timely. Schedulers are making appointments the first time around. They have mastered the process. They have time to pre-register the patient properly and with more detail. Errors in pre-registration have dropped dramatically.

Bottlenecks and patient complaints are a thing of the past. As an added bonus, the new workflow model has done a lot for team building. The employees now depend on each other to get the job done and care for the patients. Morale has never been better!

The Secrets

1. When complaints are chronic, address them.
2. When volume demands it, centralize functions and streamline processes.
3. Minimize front office interruptions.
4. Remove clerical tasks from nursing staff.
5. Centralizing doesn't take additional staff.
6. Patient flow problems reduce productivity.
7. Centralization improves teamwork.
8. When an administrator and consultant team up the results can be amazing.

FORMS ADDED TO YOUR TOOLBOX:

֍ *Telephone Appointment Tracking* (p. 149)
֍ *Clinical Telephone Tracking* (p. 150)
֍ *Patient Visit Time Study* (p. 151)

CHAPTER 3

The Amazingly Productive Doctor

Time and productivity go hand-in-hand. For years, I've listened to physicians tell me how difficult it is to manage their time. They are continually and equally frustrated with not enough time and dead time—the time they are in the office, expecting to see a patient, and the exam room is empty. Through many consulting experiences and years of examining medical practice operations, I have come to believe these two time problems are equally important. After all, if you don't have enough time, it is difficult to manage the time you do have! On the other hand, if you have dead time, it's cause for concern and will result in loss of productivity and less income.

> **KEY FACT:** *Delegate tasks that do not require your expertise, and your productivity will climb at amazing speed.*

Physicians' time is often eroded because they take on things they shouldn't and the staff should! When conducting site visits, it is common to observe physicians consumed with tasks that could, with little effort and planning, be delegated to the staff. Physicians need to ask themselves, "What am I doing that eats away at my time and doesn't require my skills or judgment?" When these tasks are shifted to employees, doctors can improve their productivity, and just maybe they will actually get out of the office on time.

For many physicians, delegating is easier said then done! There are a number of reasons physicians and administrators fail to delegate, some more common than others:

- A lack of confidence in the staff's capabilities;
- Failure to train employees to assume additional responsibilities;
- The "my way is the only way" syndrome;
- It's a habit that's never been addressed;
- Fear of losing control; and
- Fear of compromising the outcome.

Most physicians, if they set their mind to it, can delegate more and enjoy the time they gain and the benefits it brings them. When staff members are well trained and understand what the physician needs and expects from them, they keep patients moving and everyone works in "real-time." Working in real-time means doing today's work today. This simplifies the day at the office and leaves less clinical work behind.

When physicians want to know what they can do to improve their time management and clinic performance, I am reminded of a long-time client of mine. There's a lot to be said for the way this practice runs its clinic sessions and spends its time.

MAKING TIME COUNT

Coastal Allergy Care, a southern California adult and pediatric allergy practice, is progressive. Staff members always look ahead to see if they can do things better, investing in tools and technology to improve service to their patients while at the same time making their jobs easier. During the past 20 years, the practice has grown to include two physicians and a nurse practitioner, with three offices strategically positioned throughout the region.

When problems puzzle members of this busy practice or they feel direction is needed, they don't hesitate to seek professional help. However, when it comes to optimizing physician productivity no help is needed. The practice shines, and there is much to learn about how it does this.

Coastal Allergy has it wired! The smart use of ancillary staff and effective delegation make for smooth clinical flow and good physician time management. I have been amazed at its ability to make the most of each day. This has allowed the practice to reach productivity numbers that far exceed the average allergy practice.

Coastal relies on its entire clinical staff to keep doctors moving and patients cared for and to complete the day's tasks in real-time. It orchestrates clinic sessions with incredible efficiency and productivity. This was the case long before it converted to electronic medical records (EMRs) two years ago.

The nurses now have computers, but in the past they scribed the old-fashioned way. EMRs have given them the ability to become even more efficient. This additional technology reduces paperwork, provides easy access to information and further enhances productivity.

THE CLINICAL FLOW

This is what I saw as I observed Lewis Kanter, M.D., the practice's founder, and his clinical staff as they went about their day. There are three nurses working with the doctor during his clinic session. Two are shadowing with him, while the other is performing skin tests, providing allergy shots for other patients and lending whatever support is needed.

These nurses not only perceive the needs of the doctor, they perceive the needs of each other. One nurse picks up where the other leaves off. It's amazing to watch. It's like a dance, and it is often orchestrated with very little dialogue. It's obvious that this clinical staff is skilled and has been well trained. They are confident, know what needs to be done and support the physician. They are working to their potential and are given the opportunity to enrich their knowledge and skills—so they can better serve the practice and the patients.

One nurse will escort the patient to the exam room, complete the history taking and prepare the patient for the exam, documenting all this on the computer in real-time. Computers are everywhere—in each exam room, at the nurses' station, in the doctors' offices and in various locations in the business office.

When a doctor is ready to enter the exam room, he can be assured that needed information will be available on the computer terminal. Just as importantly, when he goes into the exam room, a nurse will follow him. The physician reviews the history and moves on to examine the patient, at which time the nurse will sit at the computer. This allows the doctor to focus entirely on the patient. As he completes the exam, and talks about the findings, the nurse scribes, completing the chart documentation. This enables the patient to hear what the findings and impressions are. The process continues as the treatment plan is discussed, studies are ordered and prescriptions are written.

When the physician completes the visit, he is able to leave the exam room, departing with ease; moving on to the next patient, accompanied by another nurse. The first nurse stays with the patient to complete the visit and give the patient instructions. The nurse then goes on to perform whatever diagnostic tests are ordered, posts the visit charges in the computer and sees that the patient receives the proper patient aids and education materials. This is all accomplished while the physician moves on from patient to patient, making the most of his time and using the staff to his advantage. The patients love this approach to their care. They never feel rushed, and they experience a team of people looking after their needs

New patients are often in the office for up to two hours, having diagnostic procedures and skin tests after the physician consultation. Patients don't mind—because then they don't have to come back for a separate visit for the skin tests and will get into a treatment regimen that much sooner.

In addition to scribing the patient's history and exam results, nurses assume responsibility for entering the visit and diagnostic code into the computer. This is a great concept, because the nurses are in the exam room throughout the visit, hear the discussion between patient and doctor and know exactly what services have been performed and ordered.

When the patient reaches the exit station the charges are already posted, and the instructions for scheduling the next appointment have been documented. There is no need for a receptionist to leave his or her station or get on the intercom with a nurse to track down a charge ticket. This eliminates interruptions, reduces processes and speeds up workflow.

The main facility easily accommodates the ability to glide through the office session. With seven exam rooms and no more than two providers in session at the same time, it is possible to extend the patient visit to include skin tests and diagnostic studies without impeding patient flow or the physician's time.

The goal is to eliminate down time for the physicians and the nurse practitioner. From a financial perspective, they are the most valuable players on the team. With a staff that keeps the flow, they are able to capitalize on this without compromising patient care or the quality of service. This model is practical, and it makes sense.

EVERYONE BENEFITS

What does the practice gain by this team approach to patient care and physicians delegating so much in the clinical setting? For starters, more patients are seen in less time, and they aren't kept waiting.

Members of the staff enjoy their jobs and work well together, which is evident by their longevity. The average tenure for the nurses at Coastal Allergy is more than 10 years. This is a tribute to the physicians and nursing supervisor, Ketty Owens, RN. Ketty has been with the practice since

TABLE 1. Coastal Allergy Care Productivity Performance Measures*

2004 Statistics	Coastal Allergy Care	SMD/NAHC	MGMA
Gross charges	$1,436,455	$ 949,522	$1,156,693
FTE staff	5.0	4.4	6.03

*per FTE physician

FTE = full-time equivalent; MGMA = Medical Group Management Association; SMD/NAHC = Society of Medical-Dental Management Consultants/National Association of Healthcare Consultants.

its beginning. Since the cost of replacing an employee is estimated to be as much as one year's salary, reduced turnover contributes to the bottom-line.

Next, patients are well informed, and it takes less time to diagnose and resolve their clinical problems. The nonverbal communication from the clinic to the front office saves time and reduces frustration. It also reduces the potential for missing charges, missed instructions or failing to schedule a follow-up appointment.

Since the physicians and staff work in real-time, they are not plagued with batches of work that need to be completed at the end of the clinic session. In the end, patients and staff are more satisfied; there is greater productivity and higher profitability.

NUMBERS TALK

Overall, Coastal Allergy Care outperforms allergy practices nationwide, as demonstrated by the productivity performance measures (per full-time equivalent [FTE] physician) shown in Table 1.

Coastal Allergy's gross charges are 51% higher than those reported by the Society of Medical-Dental Management Consultants/National Association of Healthcare Consultants' (SMD/NAHC) median. Coastal Allergy reports .6 FTE more than SMD/NAHC, but it pays off with far greater productivity. Despite the fact that allergists listed in the Medical Group Management Association (MGMA) report reveal 6.03 employees per physician against Coastal's five, Coastal's charges exceed MGMA's by 24%.

These impressive numbers substantiate the economic benefit Coast Allergy enjoys due to the highly productive clinical model it employs. It's worth noting that Dr. Kanter is the highest producer for his group, yet he is only in clinic session an average of 24 hours a week and was out of the office 26 days last year. That is amazing!

LESSON LEARNED

Sometimes a practice focuses too much on the physician/staff ratio, when additional staff just might be the right prescription for improving practice performance. When staff members are used wisely and doctors delegate more, productivity rises, resulting in healthier profits. At a time when the healthcare dollar is continually being squeezed, this is no small feat. The old adage is true, do what you do best and leave the rest to someone else.

The Secrets

1. Take a critical look at how you manage time.
2. Train staff members to meet their potential.
3. Delegate tasks that do not require your skills.
4. Work in real-time.
5. Adding more staff can increase clinical productivity.
6. Optimize exam room utilization and clinic flow.
7. Develop a cohesive clinical team.
8. Improve physician productivity to serve patients better and increase revenue.

FORMS ADDED TO YOUR TOOLBOX:

∞ *Training Monitor* (p. 152)
∞ *The Art of Delegation* (p. 153)

CHAPTER 4

Mastering the Appointment Schedule

All's well that ends well, but sometimes the road to get there has some unexpected twists and turns. Such is the way when it comes to mastering the appointment schedule. Over the years, most medical practices, regardless of their size or specialty, have struggled in search of a way to fine-tune the appointment schedule. Somehow it never seems quite right. The doctor doesn't stay on schedule and rarely gets out of the office on time. When this happens, everyone pays the price: the physicians, patients and staff. Unfortunately, it's not uncommon.

KEY FACT: *Stay on time and work in "real-time" with scheduling techniques that meet patient demands.*

For some practices, managing the appointment system seems like an impossible feat. The phone rings off the hook with patients that need appointments, some more urgent than others. Every day, staff members end up double-booking sick patients when the next "real" opening on the books is three weeks away. Suzanne Johnson, M.D., a busy primary care physician from Texas, experienced these same problems. She struggled with the way patients were scheduled. There were never enough hours in the day, and patients sometimes waited weeks to get an appointment. Adding a mid-level provider was helpful, but it didn't solve the problem for this popular physician. Patients seemed willing to wait to see her, despite their frustration at the long delay. The practice tried a variety of techniques to sooth the problem, but just couldn't get a handle on managing the appointment system. Finally Dr. Johnson looked for a consultant to examine the situation and come up with a solution.

LOOKING AT THE INDICATORS

I began the investigation with a search for the next available appointment and discovered that the first opening for an established patient was in eight days, with 18 days for a new patient. If someone wanted an annual exam, the wait was 100 days. A review of the previous week's schedule revealed a pattern of double-booking three to five appointment slots each day. The receptionist told me there was no other choice. Patients that didn't schedule because of the long wait sometimes ended up calling back in a few days because they didn't get better and "had to get in." Sick patients were getting crammed into an already full schedule. It didn't take a genius to realize that the demand for appointments far exceeded existing capabilities.

Next, I observed the clinical staff members working through their day. The reception and exam rooms were full. The physician and nurse practitioner fell further and further behind. In an attempt to get back on schedule, they let their charting go until the end of the day and ended up leaving a stack of work behind for the next day.

When I clocked the wait time for patients, it averaged 35 minutes—from scheduled appointment time until they were actually roomed, coupled with an additional wait of at least 15 minutes once they were in the exam room. No wonder the staff welcomed the no-show patient. With this kind of backlog, they rarely got out of the office on time. Staff members voiced concern about how much overtime they were putting in.

The findings were telling. The classic symptoms of an unmanaged scheduling system were a reality for this hard-working practice:

1. Demand greater than access, delaying the time it takes for patients to get an appointment;
2. Frequent double-booking of appointments;
3. More than an occasional no-show or late cancellation;
4. Long wait times for patients once they arrived in the office;
5. Physician getting out of the office late, mid-day and evening;
6. Charting incomplete at the end of the day; and
7. Continual staff overtime.

GETTING TO THE ROOT OF THE PROBLEM

Now it was time to dig deeper. I proceeded by examining 30 random daily schedules from the previous three months, looking for underlying factors and getting answers to these critical questions:
- How many patients were actually seen each day?
- Were there variables in the daily patient load?
- Was the demand greater on specific days or particular times of the day?

• What trends were contributing to the overall problems?

The analysis revealed erratic scheduling patterns, but several trends were detected. Typically, more patients were double-booked in the late mornings and late afternoons, and nearly twice as many work-ins were added to the schedule on Mondays. The cancellations and no-shows were scattered through the day and throughout the week, elevated slightly on Fridays. The missed appointments averaged at least seven a day, nearly double the amount of work-ins.. The variables in daily production when both providers worked ranged from a low of $2,836 to a high of $3,984, more than a 40% differential. If the high of $3,984 became the benchmark, this practice would realize a substantial gain in net revenue.

The physician's amount of time out of the office impeded overall production. Even though Dr. Johnson's typical schedule consisted of eight half-day sessions a week, with a day off at mid-week, she averaged three additional sessions off per month for various personal and business reasons. This did not include the seven holidays and six weeks out the previous year for vacation and continuing education.

I reviewed the existing scheduling templates to assess how effective they were. There were four different types of patient visits being scheduled:

1. New patient: 30 minutes;
2. Established patient: 15 minutes;
3. Pre-employment physical: 45 minutes; and
4. Annual physical: 60 minutes.

I needed to determine whether these time slots were realistic. How much time did each of the appointment types "really" need, and did the physician and nurse practitioner require the same amount of time?

For a period of 10 days, the nurses and the providers marked the charge ticket for each patient seen in the office. The nurses indicated the type of patient visit, and both the physician and nurse practitioner documented the actual time they spent with the patient. This information helped determine how realistic the existing templates were and if they needed to be revamped.

The findings revealed that the physician spent less time with patients then the schedule indicated (Figure 1). This held true for the nurse practitioner as well, with the exception of established patients. The greatest disparity for both providers was the annual physical, where the schedule dedicated 60 minutes, far more than either provider required. Many of the

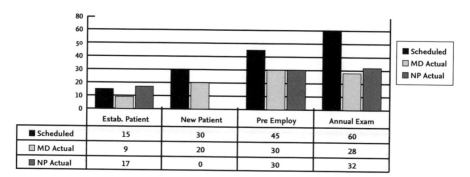

	Estab. Patient	New Patient	Pre Employ	Annual Exam
■ Scheduled	15	30	45	60
☐ MD Actual	9	20	30	28
■ NP Actual	17	0	30	32

FIGURE 1. Time dedicated to each patient type.

work-in patients presented with one symptom: a rash, earache, mole check or a common cold. These patients required less then 10 minutes of the provider's time.

The traditional 15-minute incremental appointments just weren't appropriate and didn't provide the flexibility needed to match the actual time providers were spending with patients. Shifting to a schedule with 10-minute increments and revising the appointment time parameters would give the practice needed flexibility. Greater capacity and improved access would follow.

I then asked the receptionist to track the number of patients that were not being accommodated when they called and requested an appointment. For 10 days she kept a log that revealed five to nine patients that could not be fit into the schedule each day. Some of these patients would simply forget about it, but for others it resulted in telephone messages for the doctor and "telephone medicine."

Additional data were obtained from the practice management system to capture the monthly volume of new patients, established patients and patients needing annual exams seen by each provider. This helped clarify how to structure the new templates, based on volume and patient type.

THE FINANCIAL IMPACT

The lost revenue from no-shows and late cancellations was assessed by calculating the average visit charge, multiplied by the average number of lost appointments, subtracting the revenue gained from the double-booked patients. The estimated annual loss of revenue for missed appointments turned out to be more than $125,000. This certainly got the attention of the physician.

TABLE 1. Time Out of Office Comparative Study

	Vacation CME	Holidays	Cancelled Sessions	Total Sessions Out	Above Typical PCP	*Estimated Lost Revenue
The practice	6 weeks = 48 sessions	7 days = 14 sessions	30 sessions	92	38	$62,774
Typical PCP	4 weeks = 32 sessions	7 = days 14 sessions	8 sessions	54	N/A	N/A

*Lost revenue calculated based on primary care average charges from the Society of Medical-Dental Management Consultants/National Association of Healthcare Consultants 2004 national statistics. CME = continuing medical education; PCP = primary care physician.

Additional revenue of more than $62,000 could be captured if Dr. Johnson worked the same number of sessions as the typical primary care physician (Table 1).

The unmanaged schedule also contributed to the cost of overtime wages for the practice. Each receptionist clocked in an average of 15 hours a month in overtime, and each nurse as much as 22 hours per month, for an estimated $72,000 a year.

The annual financial loss was projected to be more than $250,000 a year. There were other considerations that cost the practice as well. First were patients, both new and established, scheduling elsewhere because of poor access. These patients were unlikely to return, representing a long-term loss to the practice. Second, the unmanaged scheduling system resulted in less-satisfied patients, generating word-of mouth damage to the reputation of the practice and loss of future referrals.

DEFINING THE OBJECTIVES

The analysis pinpointed the impact of an unmanaged appointment schedule and crystallized in everyone's mind the issues that needed to be resolved. Three primary objectives were outlined.

1. Improve access
2. Develop a manageable scheduling system
   a. Create valid templates
   b. Balance demand with capacity
   c. Stay on time
   d. Reduce no-show and late-cancellation rates
3. Improve time management

a. Stay on time

b. Reduce overtime

Staff buy-in was critical to accomplishing these objectives. Achieving the stated goals required a dramatic shift in the way patients were handled and how they were scheduled. It took a leap of faith for Dr. Johnson and her staff to imagine balancing demand with capacity, staying on schedule and getting out of the office on time.

Ten more patients could be seen each day if no-shows were reduced to a minimum and a tighter scheduling system was developed. Furthermore, access would improve immediately, and the need to double-book would soon vanish. This would go a long way toward getting control over the scheduling system and getting everyone out of the office on time.

MASTERING THE SCHEDULE

Providers were spending between 9 and 32 minutes with each patient. Some of these patients had a simple ear infection and others had chronic conditions and multiple health problems. The new template needed to have the flexibility to meet these variations. Based on the objective data collected and meetings with the nurses and the providers, three types of appointments were developed—"quik-chek," standard, and complex—based on 10-minute increments up to 30 minutes (Table 2).

Implementing these appointment times and time parameters, along with better management of missed appointments, would yield sufficient gains to hold slots for same-day appointments. This would enable the practice

TABLE 2. Types of Appointments

Quik-Chek (10 minutes)	Standard (20 minutes)	Complex (30 minutes)
• Single symptom — Rash/mole — Ear infection — Blood pressure check • Simple recheck • Minor complaints	• Multiple symptoms • Infections • Established patient with chronic problems • Monitoring patient with multiple problems • New patient with minor complaints	• Annual exam • Pre-employment physical • Established patient with complications • New patient with chronic or major complaints

to adequately accommodate new patients and manage the existing patient load appropriately.

A modified open-access system emerged—a system that would accommodate appointments the same day patients requested them. The bulk of pre-scheduled appointments were expected to be for new patients, annual exams and re-checks. To avoid the historical Monday crunch, employment physicals and annual exams would not be scheduled on Mondays. This would result in improved workflow and better time management.

When finalized, the new template placed a hold on 22 10-minute appointment slots per day, releasing them at noon on the prior day. A number of the openings were concurrent, allowing staff to schedule quik-cheks or standard appointments, depending on the needs of the patient. These open slots would go a long way in meeting the historical pent-up demand that kept as many as nine patients a day from getting appointments in the past and the practice of double-booking an average of four patients a day. Besides this, the practice would be better positioned to add new patients, handle growth and manage the day.

In order to accommodate pent-up demand and improve access immediately, the providers were asked to expand their daily schedule by one hour for the first six weeks to eliminate a future backlog. At the end of the six-week period, it was expected that demand and capacity would be balanced, and same-day appointments would be readily available for patients. The provider's would then be able to return to their regular hours.

The new templates were presented at a staff meeting. When staff members realized there would be added capacity and more open appointments, they were motivated and supported the new scheduling system.

Preparing for Implementation

Getting a handle on missed appointments was a critical factor in maximizing the schedule. The general lack of regard for scheduled appointments had to be addressed. Everyone (providers, staff and patients) needed to respect and honor scheduled appointments. This meant changing behavior and attitudes. This needed to happen to reduce the missed appointment rate before implementing the new scheduling system.

The manager and I prepared several pre-implementation in-services to overcome potential obstacles and reassure the staff. The first in-service covered the consequences of missed appointments and how the staff could help us lower the no-show rate by taking control of the schedule. Patients needed to view their appointments as a priority, and staff needed to send patients this message. Telephone scripts were prepared and used for role-playing. They included what to say and what not to say when confirming appointments or handling the no-show. We wanted to be sure the staff didn't send out subliminal messages giving patients permission to ignore an appointment or cancel at the last minute.

I took this opportunity to review the economic impact of no-shows and last-minute cancellations to help everyone understand how costly missed appointments are—not only financially, but also the disruption and loss of control that no-shows and double-booking causes. I assured the staff members that they had the power to reduce missed appointments and explained the benefits they would gain: manageable workflow, less disruption and predictable days. I provided the schedulers with the Appointment Power Words Matrix to guide them with booking, confirming appointments and handling patients with other scheduling issues. The message was clear— take control of the schedule to improve financial performance and manage patient flow.

The clinical staff worked with the manager in developing tools to guide the schedulers in adapting to the new templates and open-access system. It was important for the schedulers to know what questions to ask patients to determine if they should schedule a quik-chek or standard appointment. The nurses developed cue cards with a list of probing questions for the schedulers to ask the patient. Together the staff participated in an interactive workshop, discussing various elements of the open-access system, how the patients were likely to respond, how the templates would work, the transition time frame and the importance of communicating and working together to fine-tune the process during the implementation.

The nurses agreed to provide additional assistance and further training for the schedulers during the adjustment period:

1. If the scheduler was unsure of what type of an appointment to schedule, the call was transferred to a nurse.
2. The nurses conducted weekly reviews with the schedulers. This provided an opportunity for open dialogue to further educate the schedulers, review the previous week's schedule and discuss problems that emerged and appointments that were questionable. This was a continuing education process that strengthened the schedulers' skills and confidence.

Managing the new templates effectively required optimizing the provider's time with patients. Nurses needed to do their part to have patients properly prepared for each visit. With the guidance of the manager, the providers and nurses developed a Rooming Matrix. It listed the reason for the visit, the chief complaints and the requirements needed to prepare a patient for the exam, based on the reason for the visit. For example, an annual physical would require checking weight, height, blood pressure, temperature, respirations and pulse. The nurse would also need to review medication, check allergies, obtain urine and blood samples and instruct the patient to completely undress and put on a full gown.

On the other hand, a patient with a dermatologic rash or mole would simply need to have his or her blood pressure and temperature taken, be questioned about allergies and be instructed to undress as required to expose the area. The nurse would also need to ask how long the patient had the condition and if it was painful or itched.

In order to make the most of the exam rooms and improve flow, patient instructions and education needed to take place elsewhere. A small storage room was converted into a patient education center. One of the nurses assumed responsibility for getting the center equipped with brochures and videos from pharmaceutical and equipment companies. Patient instructions, consent forms and other such materials were organized in files. This room became a vital factor in keeping the providers on schedule. When patients needed special instructions or materials at the conclusion of the visit, a nurse would take them to the center, complete the visit and answer their questions. This freed the exam room for the next patient and allowed the doctor or nurse practitioner to move on to the next patient.

The Implementation

The final step was placing the new templates in the computer system. Because the appointment calendar was booked until March 15th, the target date for implementation was set for May 1. Patients scheduling beyond May 1 would be scheduled using the new template. In the meantime, the schedulers worked to reduce missed appointments. In mid-April, patients were sent an announcement of same-day scheduling availability. The providers also expanded their schedule by one hour beginning May 1. Weekly meetings were held to keep communication open and make any adjustments that might be required during the first 30 days.

Monitoring the Results

A patient satisfaction survey conducted before implementing the new scheduling system served as a baseline, followed by quarterly surveys the first year and annually thereafter.

Once the implementation process began, progress was closely observed. Everyone needed to stay on top of the schedule and take a critical look at what caused delays, taking steps to avoid a recurring pattern. Missed appointments were tracked, revealing a marked decrease in no shows and last minute cancellations. Follow-up time studies were conducted for three months straight to examine the progress being made with patient access and wait times.

The practice management reports tracked productivity—patient visits and charges for both the physician and the nurse practitioner—and payroll records revealed changes in overtime costs.

CHECKING OUT THE GAINS

The success of the revised appointment system was evident with the improvement in patient flow and access. Physician and staff efficiency skyrocketed. Tangible results at the six-month mark were proof that the practice had mastered the scheduling system:

- Patients were roomed within five minutes of arrival 93% of the time.
- Same-day access was available for established patients with the exception of annual exams.
- New-patient visits were scheduled within five days.
- Annual exams and pre-employment physicals were scheduled within seven days.
- No-shows and late cancellations were reduced by 70%.
- Patient satisfaction with obtaining appointments went from 25% to 87%.
- Overtime was under control, cutting payroll costs by more than $5,000/month.
- Revenue increased by 22%.
- Physicians and staff got out of the office on time more than 90% of the time.

The first six weeks were difficult, and the results were not evident for several months. During this time, some simple modifications to the original plan were required. The manager encountered a lack of confidence with some employees and minor resistance from one individual. A fair amount of reassurance and reinforcement was necessary before things stabilized. But in the end, everyone agreed it was well worth it!

The Secrets

1. There are classic symptoms of an unmanaged scheduling system.
2. Templates based on actual needs increase productivity and time management.
3. Missed appointments are costly to the practice.
4. Careful planning and staff involvement is essential to designing and implementing a realistic scheduling system.
5. An open access scheduling system improves patient service.
6. Educate staff and give them the tools they need.
7. To gain support for change, communicate the benefits.

FORMS ADDED TO YOUR TOOLBOX:

∞ *Appointment Power Words Matrix* (p. 154)
∞ *Rooming Matrix* (p. 155)

CHAPTER 5

Commonsense Risk Management

In my work as a consultant, physicians frequently express their concerns about potential malpractice litigation. This concern has been magnified in recent years—and with good cause. Malpractice suits are on the rise, and many of them are frivolous. The resulting increases in malpractice insurance premiums take a bigger bite out of doctors' income. It's no wonder physicians across the country are taking a defensive posture when it comes to medical decision-making and managing risk.

KEY FACT: *There's more to risk management than clinical skills and clinical judgment.*

Managing risk is complex. There are, of course, clinical issues: the medical decision-making; the skill level of the physician and other care givers; and, the outcome. Most risk-prevention strategies employed are related to physicians' clinical skills: physicians keep their clinical skills sharp and are diligent about continuing medical education in order to stay on top of emerging treatments for their specialty. The hospital's peer-review and quality-assurance programs help maintain standards of clinical care to further reduce risk.

But while physicians' clinical skills are vital in caring for their patients, managing risk and avoiding lawsuits, there's another side of risk management that seldom gets the attention it deserves. It's "commonsense" risk management, and it's not related to clinical skills or clinical judgment. It's a matter of how the office runs and how patients *feel* about their physician. These are important factors in keeping you out of court!

Commonsense risk management includes the relationship you have with patients, how well you communicate, the competency and training of your staff, your documentation procedures and the office systems you have in place to track and follow-up on patients. When you fail with these things, risk increases. It hardly matters what medical school you went to or if you are the best physician in town.

COULD IT HAPPEN TO YOU?

I am reminded of a practice I worked with a few years ago and a young physician that joined the practice the previous year. We'll call him Dr. Young. He graduated from an Ivy League school with honors and trained at a prestigious medical center. His diagnostic skills were amazing, and it didn't take long for him to get firmly rooted in the practice. He got along well with his colleagues and enjoyed both the practice and the patients. His partners were ecstatic to have him aboard.

Then one day, Dr. Young received a crushing blow and knew he would be faced with his first malpractice suit. Two months earlier, Mrs. Wilson had come to the office with chest pain and difficult, labored breathing. Dr. Young ordered a chest x-ray as part of his exam. Eight weeks later, Mrs. Wilson returned, because she wasn't getting better. When Dr. Young opened the chart and looked at his notes, he quickly flipped to the report on the chest x-ray. The report presented devastating news. Mrs. Wilson had lung cancer. Somehow, the report had been filed in the chart without the doctor ever seeing it. Because Mrs. Wilson didn't get a follow-up call from Dr. Young, she assumed the x-ray results presented no problems, and she continued following his treatment plan. When her symptoms increased and she started losing weight, she scheduled another appointment.

Dr. Young was not going to be sued because he was a mediocre physician or lacked clinical judgment, but because someone didn't follow office procedures. Something slipped through the cracks. Perhaps a new and improperly trained medical records person mistakenly filed the report. Maybe the procedures for handling reports were not well defined or perhaps they were inadequate. An office malfunction compromised this patient's care, not a lack of clinical expertise. Regardless, this oversight would be construed as medical negligence. Could this happen in your office?

Medical practice managers and physicians, take heed. It's important to look at the commonsense components of risk management and decide if your practice passes muster. It may be time to get your ship in order and develop an office-based risk management plan. Following are some key common-sense risk management strategies.

START WITH THE RELATIONSHIP

Developing a strong bond with your patients reduces the risk of malpractice suits. People are more than a little reluctant to sue their friends or people they really like, regardless of the nature of the suit.

It's not your job to become friends with your patients, but you do have an obligation to be friendly with your patients. Patients are judging you based on how personable you are and if you make them feel important. They are not equipped to judge your medical skills, and they wouldn't have scheduled an appointment with you unless they thought you were competent. Now it's up to you, beginning with the first impression. On the first visit, patients begin forming their opinion, and it's your job to win them over.

Consider the First Encounter

Begin by thinking about your first encounter with the patient. It is common for physicians to act as though the entire purpose of the visit is to get to the diagnosis and treat the problem. By all means, that is your clinical mission. But don't think that satisfying your clinical mission alone will result in satisfied patients that are grateful for the care they are given. When only clinical concerns are addressed, you are treating a condition and not the person. Patients, especially new patients, want and need more from you than clinical expertise. They want to feel important and believe that you care about them. If you get off to a bad start, it will be difficult to make up for it.

Most clinicians know the importance of good eye contact and a proper introduction, but that's only the start of your interaction with the patient. There are 10 golden rules that help physicians and mid-level providers build stronger patient relationships. Your medical office should integrate these rules into training manuals, and it's also important to periodically review these rules with your staff:

1. Once you are in the exam room, sit in a chair until you begin the examination. Looking down on patients makes them feel inferior. You want patients to feel and "know" that they are equal to you.
2. Read the chart before you go in the room. If the nurse wrote the reason for the visit in the chart there is no need for you to ask the patient why he or she is there.

3. Frequently refer to patients by name. It makes them feel you are connected and care about the whole person, not just their condition.
4. Get personal. It only takes a few minutes. Ask about the patient's hobbies, job or family. If you share an interest, so much the better.
5. Apologize if you're late, but don't act rushed. Your patients deserve your time. If you are relaxed and calm, they feel they have your attention and time.
6. Do not permit staff to interrupt you when you are with a patient unless absolutely necessary. Interruptions make patients feel like they're not a priority.
7. Do not use medical jargon the patient won't understand.
8. Never ask a patient a question unless you are willing to give your full attention to listen to the response. Look at the patient when either of you are speaking. Avoid looking at the chart while conversing, and don't interrupt.
9. Once you've presented your diagnosis, treatment and follow-up plan, do not assume the patient understands everything you said. Ask for affirmation and be willing to clarify or repeat your summation or instructions.
10. Before you complete each encounter, make sure that you have answered the patient's questions. Failure to completely answer questions results in unnecessary phone calls and frustrated patients.

Going the Extra Mile

A medical practice is not a commercial enterprise like the Ritz-Carlton, Nordstrom or Southwest Airlines, each known for taking pride in going the extra mile for its customers. Just the same, medical practices can benefit greatly by going the extra mile to build stronger relationships and make patients feel important. For example, when a patient has had an office-based operative procedure or has been in the hospital, why not call the patient the following day to see how he is doing? Ask if he has any questions and provide reassurance. If a patient who comes to the office appears to be too ill to be comfortable in the reception room, immediately escort her to an exam room so she can lie down. If patients have transportation problems, investigate what dial-a-ride services are available.

How we communicate goes a long way in making patients feel comfortable and cared about. The words we use can influence the patient experience. For example using the word "you" in some contexts makes people defensive—"Why did you do that?" The Communication Matrix added to the toolbox provides concrete examples that improve communication.

Think about having someone in the office assigned to be the patient advocate. A patient advocate provides special services for patients and makes sure their needs are met. An advocate also resolves complaints and smoothes out difficult situations—tempering a storm before it gets out of control. A patient advocate certainly gives the "we care" message and builds solid relationships with patients.

DOCUMENTATION

The written word tells the story. Physicians discover this when it's time to defend their records in court. It's not just getting things documented. It's a matter of legibility, timeliness and identifying who wrote what and when. Consult your legal advisor and medical liability insurance company to give you the specifics on what you should and shouldn't include in your documentation.

DEVELOP A RISK MANAGEMENT PLAN

The risk management related to documentation also includes handling and storage of records. Avoid a disaster similar to Dr. Young's. In my experience, fewer than 10% of medical practices have a written risk management plan. Generally, training on record keeping is ad hoc and sketchy at best, and nothing is in writing. Remember the old adage, if it isn't written down, it didn't happen. This applies not only to documenting your treatment, but to the risk management strategies the practice employs. The risk management plan and staff training on risk validate your commitment to managing risk.

Risk management plans usually include:
1. Record keeping
   a. Signature requirements
   b. Release of information
   c. Purging records
2. Samples of office forms related to medical record keeping
   a. Forms for HIPAA compliance
   b. Informed consent forms
   c. Medical records release

    d. Patient registration form and emergency contact release
3. Staff documentation policy and procedures
    a. Who documents what and who signs off
    b. Documentation time requirements (i.e., within the hour, at the end of session)
    c. Punitive action for noncompliance
    d. What reports require a signature
4. Documentation and record keeping
    a. Definition of performance standards
    b. Performance measurement
    c. Quality assurance/peer review
5. Staff medical records training modules
    a. Clinicians
    b. Medical records staff
    c. Billing staff
    d. Front office
6. Tracking system and procedures
    a. Diagnostic studies ordered in office or elsewhere
    b. Reporting methods
    c. Recall system
    Missed appointments
7. Medical records audit procedures
    a. Coding and documentation
    b. Risk management
8. Discharging the noncomplaint patient
    a. Protocol
    b. Sample discharge letter

Some components of this risk management plan are specific to the practice, and others are part of most medical practices' office procedures. For example, the release of medical records and signature requirements may be clear to your staff members, but they aren't written in a formal plan. Your practice likely has a series of form letters, such as those relating to HIPAA; informed consent forms; and other forms important to record keeping for patients, and these forms may not exist in one master manual. Your challenge is to set standards, define punitive actions and develop medical record training modules. When preparing a risk management plan, practices often discover their tracking and recall systems could use fine-tuning.

Setting Standards

Setting standards with documentation and record keeping begins with physicians respecting the medical chart. If they don't respect it, how can they expect the staff to do so? Staff members of one practice told me they couldn't find records that were in the trunk of a doctor's car because he took a stack home over the weekend to get caught up on "last week's" dictation.

In the future, the use of electronic health records (EHR) will improve our ability to standardize office practices, improving documentation and accountability. In the meantime, it is still important to address these issues.

Begin setting performance standards by focusing on that which most directly influences the patient's safety and medical care, as well as that which might be construed as negligence on the practice's part. Start with the top priority items and create a list. Here are a few examples, but each practice should prepare a list of standards based on its standard protocol. If standard protocols are not in place, develop them now.

Rooming a patient: What specific items is the nurse/medical assistant to document when rooming a patient? Naturally, this will vary by specialty and type of appointment, but may include: date; vital signs, temperature and weight; presenting symptoms and duration; medications; and initialing the documentation.

Responding to patient phone calls (clinical): What documentation and actions are required for handling incoming clinical telephone calls? Is it a double-entry system or a duplicate system with the original placed in the chart? Are the date and time of call, primary and secondary phone numbers, symptoms and temperature recorded? Are the initials of the person who took the message recorded? Who is the information routed to and how is it routed? When is the call considered emergent and routed to a nurse/doctor? What should the caller be told about when to expect a reply? (This should be consistent and reliable.) What is the maximum time before the call is returned?

Documenting the visit: What are your requirements for physicians and mid-level providers regarding documentation—scribes, dictation, handheld or by hand? What are your legibility and signature requirements? Do you have dictation sign-off requirements (i.e., date dictated, date transcribed)? Do you have time limits for dictation, transcription, typed/signed and in the chart? What are your rules on physician chart handling, the need for charts to remain on the premises and when a chart must be released to return to files? Define limits for holding on to charts.

Patient's rights and confidentiality: What is the practice's responsibility and what are the patient's rights with respect to their medical record, specifically access to information, release of information and costs for duplication?

Use these few examples as a starting point for meeting with physicians and staff to agree on documentation requirements and responsibilities. Once you have finalized the measurements, set the standard. For example, are phone calls to be transferred immediately when they seem emergent or should they be written up and routed to the nurse for action within 10 minutes? Are other clinical calls to be returned within one to two hours? Is dictation to be completed by the end of the session and in the chart within 24 hours? Make decisions and set policy!

Punitive Measures

When the standards are formalized and become part of the risk management plan, establish a method to monitor compliance. Will you pull random charts and have a monthly or bi-monthly audit to check dictation or legibility of the provider and whether entries are initialed? Will you use the duplicate telephone log to pull random phone calls to see how they were handled? Beyond this, the plan needs to outline punitive measures as well as define when punitive actions are appropriate—on the first occurrence, the third or the tenth? This can be a political tightrope, but these components are essential in an effective plan. The four key elements to developing the standards are:

1. Identifying the standards;
2. Determining the measurement;
3. Developing a method to monitor compliance; and
4. Creating accountability with well-defined punitive actions.

Staff Training Guides

Developing staff training guides is easier once you have developed standards. The standards become the blueprint to help you develop training guides for each department. In addition to using the training guides for medical records and documentation as part of your risk management program, your plan should also include training on communication and customer service. Each staff member must understand his or her role in building and maintaining strong relationships with patients.

Tracking Systems

Tracking systems are important to ensure that follow-up studies and exams are ordered and completed. It's also important for ensuring that you obtain results for biopsies and lab work you send out of the office.

Some of the tracking in the medical office can be done with the computer, and, fortunately, most practices have a computerized practice management system. These systems usually include an appointment-scheduling module with a recall system that can automatically send patients reminders. Most systems also have the capability to pull reports for specific conditions that need follow-up. With an electronic medical record, you have even greater tracking capabilities. Computerized systems are the most reliable tracking systems. But remember, you have to put the information in to be able to sort the data and get the reports you need. The reliability of any system still depends on the people using it.

Many practices have a computer system for billing, but fail to explore its tracking capabilities. If you have a computer and you aren't using it for recall and tracking missed appointments, it's time to meet with your vendor and explore the system's tracking tools. If your system is limited, there are products on the market that can be integrated with existing computer systems to automate patient reminders and appointment confirmation. It's certainly worth exploring your options.

Other tracking systems are manual. For diagnostic studies that are ordered, a manual log is easy to implement and does a good job of tracking. Create a log with columns to write the patient's name, date, tests ordered, what facility is performing the study and the date the report is received. The reliability of such a system depends on staff documenting in real-time. As soon as the order is given, log it in; as soon as the report is received, log it in. Monitor the log, and when reports are not received within the standard time, place a call and get them faxed over immediately. Once the report is logged in, follow proper procedures to see that it is read and initialed by the doctor and that the patient has been informed. These procedures should be written in your risk management plan.

A "tickler" filer is another typical manual system that consists of an index card on each patient that is being tracked for a specific purpose. Key information will be documented on the card, including the follow-up date. The index cards are then kept in a master card box by month/week for follow-up. This is a common practice for following up on breast exams, mammograms, Pap smears and other rechecks. An accordion file system is sometimes used in a similar way, keeping the order sheet for follow-up studies in a tickler file by month.

Many practices have electronic messaging or "telephone in" service. This gives the patient access to test results. When tests are ordered, the patient is given a card with a phone number to access the system and a time frame to call for the test results. Once the test results are received, the doctor notes the findings and makes comments on the report. The nurse then records a message in the system for the patient to hear. There are obvious benefits to electronic reporting of results: it is more productive for the office than mailing, gives the patient control and is confidential.

When it comes to tracking, computer systems have come a long way, and there are many products that work with existing practice management systems. If you are not fully automated, now would be a good time to advance your use of technology. Consider these technologies as an opportunity to strengthen your risk management efforts.

In any tracking system, staff members need to understand the importance of the system and how to use and manage it. If an office system fails, one of the first questions a plaintiff's attorney will ask will relate to the adequacy of employee orientation. The training guide and risk management plan you develop will be your defense.

DISCHARGING PATIENTS

It's difficult to make a decision to discharge a patient. It's a very big decision, like firing an employee. Most physicians and managers avoid it until they see no alternative. But, just like terminating an employee, if it isn't dealt with when the signs first become evident, you may regret it later. A noncompliant patient represents a risk to the practice. So does the patient that is antagonistic to the point where the physician-patient relationship deteriorates. The most common reasons for discharging a patient are:

- Noncompliance related to medical treatment;
- Abrasive, abusive or threatening behavior; and
- Noncompliance with payment for services.

Regardless of the reason, when the practice determines it is time to sever the relationship, it is important to proceed with cautious, but decisive actions.

Physicians are obligated to continue treating a patient until the patient's condition no longer warrants treatment or the patient discharges the physician. When the physician terminates the relationship, it is important to take specific steps that ensure the patient is not abandoned:

- Do not withdraw from caring for a patient in the midst of a medical crisis.
- Verbally discharge the patient in person.
- Confirm the discharge in a letter signed by the physician.
- Establish a date for termination, depending on the patient's condition and availability of a qualified physician to take over the patient's care; usually this is somewhere between 2 weeks and 30 days.
- Describe the patient's current condition.
- Inform the patient of the need to select another physician.
- Indicate whether follow-up care should be immediate.
- Indicate prognosis if follow-up care is not obtained.
- Inform the patient of other physicians qualified to provide care.
- Let the patient know you are available for emergencies or to treat acute conditions in the interim.
- Inform the patient that the practice will provide copies of his or her medical record to the patient's new physician upon receiving written authorization and that you are available to consult with the new physician if requested.
- Send the letter by certified mail, return receipt requested.
- File the mail receipt in the patient's chart once it is received.
- Inform the staff not to schedule another appointment once the transition time has ended and follow up by flagging the patient's account in the computer system.

I offer a word of caution in handling the noncompliant patient when it involves payment for services. Once an account is considered noncollectible, do not allow staff to turn the account over to a collection agency until the physician has reviewed the chart. This allows the doctor to determine if, based on the patient relationship or medical condition, such actions would aggravate the patient in a way that might pose the threat of a malpractice suit.

TAPPING INTO RISK MANAGEMENT RESOURCES

Managers and physicians need to build a strong alliance with their malpractice insurance carriers. You share the same goal: avoiding a malpractice lawsuit. Ask your carrier if they will conduct a risk prevention audit and what risk prevention tools they can provide for the office. These carriers will usually offer you additional assistance in determining what types of continuing education on risk management are available to you.

ATTITUDES

Risk management is a silent duty. Unfortunately, the silence sometimes doesn't get the practice's attention until a problem emerges. It's far better to take a pro-active posture to avoid problems. Yes, developing a risk management plan requires time and effort. Because of this, physicians and staff may view such a project as a pain or nuisance, or may put it on the back burner until it's too late. Don't place yourself in that position. Physicians and managers that initiate and endorse the development of a risk management plan will be glad they made the effort. Make commonsense risk management a priority!

The Secrets

1. Focus on the patient relationship from the first visit.
2. Patients form their opinion about their doctors based on people skills, not clinical skills.
3. The entire practice plays a role in risk prevention.
4. Employ commonsense risk management strategies.
5. There are specific requirements to properly discharge a patient.
6. Establish standards and measurements for medical record keeping.
7. Turn to your malpractice insurance carrier for guidance and support.
8. A risk management plan is vital to protecting your practice.

FORMS ADDED TO YOUR TOOLBOX:

→ *Communication Matrix* (p. 156)
→ *Tracking Log for Diagnostic Studies* (p. 157)
→ *Sample Discharge Letter* (p. 158)

CHAPTER 6

Team Spirit— Team Power

Teams, teams and more teams—there's a lot of hype about teams and the importance for everyone in the office to feel like they are part of the team. When I look at the way most practices function, I nearly always see teams. Unfortunately, those teams don't always represent the entire practice as one unit, one team. Teams in the medical office are too often special interest groups—rather than a united team representing the interests of the entire practice. Staff members work collaboratively within each department and have common goals, but fail to pursue the global goals of the practice or consider the needs of other departments. These special interest groups may or may not have an understanding or respect for the contribution others bring to the practice.

> **KEY FACT:** *Team building is a series of empowering steps that unite staff and physicians in shared goals.*

The unity of a medical practice depends on all departments working as a unified team—and it starts at the top. The physicians must be the driving force. If they don't function as members of a team and help create a team culture, the practice will never reach its potential and the staff will not fully commit to the practice.

Midtown Ophthalmology Medical Group understands the value of "the team" and what it can do for the practice. Staff members share their goals, work hard to achieve them and celebrate their successes, all signs of a good team. But it wasn't always that way.

A few years ago, each of the 13 doctors at Midtown looked after his or her own interests; each focused on his schedule, his patients and the things he wanted to accomplish. The physicians came into the office, saw their patients and went on about their business. The practice didn't have a clear direction, but each physician knew what he wanted for himself. Competing priorities kept each of them acting like 13 individual practices instead of one group practice with 13 physicians. The physicians failed to recognize the practice's true potential as a group.

Jonathan, the practice administrator, handled the administrative responsibilities to the physicians' satisfaction. He met with the doctors each month and provided detailed updates on the state of the practice. The only group numbers getting much attention concerned the shared operating expenses. Each physician's interest was otherwise limited to his own production and revenue—"group performance" was of little concern.

Without a vision of the practice's future, things just seemed mechanical. The practice meandered along on happenstance rather than being driven by team thinking and planning. Then an interesting thing happened—the administrator resigned.

As might be expected, the physicians were nervous about replacing someone that had been with the practice for 15 years. I was hired to conduct the search and guide the selection process. The response to the search efforts brought forth some impressive candidates. Rigorous screening and testing techniques were employed to improve the odds of making the right choice. Five people made the final cut. They all had a bachelor's degree and a minimum of five years' experience managing a group medical practice. Three of them were certified medical practice executives (CMPE) through the Medical Group Management Association's American College of Medical Practice Executives (ACMPE).

When the final interviews were completed, the physicians selected Mary, a CMPE, to be the new administrator. Mary's previous employers remarked on her outstanding leadership and organizational skills, and praised her communication skills and ability to work with staff. The physicians would soon discover what a wise choice they made in hiring Mary.

Mary rolled up her sleeves and learned all about the practice, spending time with each employee and each physician to find out what made them tick. She took a cautious approach with everyone, being sensitive to the difficulty they might have adjusting to a new manager after 15 years. She respected the staff members and gave them a little space while she did her own analysis of the practice and its culture.

It didn't take long for Mary to realize that despite a fairly smooth operation, an underlying problem inhibited Midtown Ophthalmology's success. The practice lacked clear direction and didn't know where it wanted to go or how it would get there. There were a lot of people doing their jobs, including the physicians, but they weren't a team. It seemed each person went off in his own direction without concern for how his actions might impact the entire practice.

IT TAKES A LEADER

It takes a leader to build a team. With Mary at the helm, Midtown Ophthalmology now had its leader. Mary had expertise, confidence and enthusiasm, and within a few months she had earned the respect and cooperation of both the physicians and the staff. Mary knew that if she could get the physicians thinking and working like a team, the staff would soon follow. Physician leadership is critical in developing a team culture and a more unified practice.

TEAM THINKING

Because building a team culture begins with the physicians, Mary asked the physicians to agree to participate in a mission retreat, at which time they could collectively (team thinking) establish a mission and vision statement for the practice. She skillfully presented her case to the physicians, convincing them of the importance of developing a united front and how this would empower the staff and create far greater results for the practice.

Getting Buy-In

In order to persuade the physicians of the value of the retreat, Mary prepared a report on the practice's performance, beginning with human resource performance data from the previous year on overtime, staff turnover and absenteeism; all areas of under performance indicating inefficiency, a lack of commitment and/or poor morale. If the practice built a team culture, employee performance could show remarkable improvement. Next, Mary presented a picture of the practice's financial performance including productivity, income, expenses and accounts receivable data. Midtown was performing at the national average when compared with National Association of Healthcare Consultants/Society of Medical-Dental Management Consultants (NAHC/SMD) national statistics and MGMA's cost survey, but Midtown had the potential to move those numbers upward if the physicians and staff members set their mind to it. Finally, the physicians agreed to participate in a mission retreat.

Because these physicians were not accustomed to looking out for each other, cutting through the special interests of each physician during the retreat had the potential to be a political minefield. Building mutual confidence and developing an atmosphere of trust and cooperation were key. Only then would the physicians achieve the objective of the retreat: to establish and support a shared mission and vision statement.

BUILDING FROM THE GROUND UP

I assisted Mary with planning and conducting the retreat. As part of the planning process, I conducted confidential interviews in order to learn more about the physicians at Midtown Ophthalmology. Additionally, each physician was asked to complete a questionnaire to examine his or her observations and opinions. We needed the answers to key questions:

- What did they want (or expect) from the practice?
- What did they see as the practice's strengths and weaknesses?
- Did they perceive one of their colleagues as a leader—and if so, who?
- What were their personal and professional goals?

The survey went further to explore other topics in order to understand each physician's personality, working style and lifestyle. We explored wide-ranging topics, such as their attitudes toward advancing their professional skills and their interests and personal goals. This process provided a better understanding of the physicians, their perceptions and values. The survey results were a perfect guide for discussion at the retreat. These results would promote full physician participation and steer the discussion away from potential power plays.

THE RETREAT BEGINS

We kicked-off the retreat with a Friday evening social hour—an opportunity for the physicians to engage in casual conversation away from work and to become comfortable in a social setting limited to their partners.

The next morning, Mary strategically arranged the seating assignment for the retreat, placing each doctor next to the person she had the least interaction with in the past. The meeting agenda and rules of discussion were reviewed including:

- Time limits were set for each discussion point;
- No interruptions were allowed;
- Discussion must relate to the agenda topic item;

- Criticism must be kept constructive;
- For each concern, a potential solution needed to be suggested; and
- Each physician was expected to participate equally.

I presented the findings from the survey and interviews to begin an open dialogue about the interests and strengths of the physicians. I further suggested that with this information Midtown could draw on individual talents to serve the entire group.

At this point, the Great Egg Drop was introduced as a warm-up exercise. This was designed to get everyone using their individual talents in small groups that encouraged creative use of resources. Three teams were formed, and each was assigned the task of building a single egg package that could sustain a fall of eight feet. Each team was given a small set of supplies including straws, tape, the egg, a piece of cardboard and a few miscellaneous natural materials. Each team discussed why it selected the particular packaging design and then conducted the egg fall. The exercise concluded with a discussion about the reasons one team's package succeeded and another's did not. The project took less than an hour and demonstrated team brainstorming, planning, decision-making and working toward a shared goal in a nonthreatening environment.

Now that the physicians were opening up with effective sharing of ideas and information, we began working our way through the agenda. With the introduction of each topic, a healthy exchange of communication occurred. The physicians openly discussed their perceptions and concerns—things they had never talked about before. Sensitive issues, avoided in the past, were now open for discussion. They began talking about their future, what the practice meant to each of them and the real purpose of the practice.

By the end of the retreat, the physicians had achieved a unified position. They created a mission and vision statement they all truly believed in and could share with enthusiasm. Over the weekend, this team pulled together and was on its way to forming a group culture. The success of the retreat became the foundation for building the team.

STRENGTHENING THE TEAM

Under Mary's direction, Midtown Ophthalmology set a new course. After the retreat, she scheduled a staff meeting, which all the physicians attended—a major shift from the past. The physicians discussed the retreat and how they had arrived at a practice mission and vision statement. They talked about the importance of staff in helping them live the mission. T-shirts with the mission statement written across the front were passed out to everyone. For the first time, the staff felt a sense of pride and camaraderie with the physicians.

To emphasize the significance of the mission statement and the unity it represented, the statement was written in calligraphy, framed and placed in the reception room, staff lounge and conference room. The mission statement would also be placed on the home page of the practice's web site, which was under development.

Over the next few months, Mary continued the team building efforts by selecting teams of different physicians and staff to work together on practice projects. Cross-department committees further strengthened the team. Staff developed ideas to improve efficiency during monthly brown-bag brainstorming sessions. Movie tickets were given for ideas that were put into motion.

Mary acted to maintain momentum. She involved staff members in administrative tasks that enriched their job skills and kept them excited about their work. When they decided to explore upgrading their computer system's capabilities to include electronic medical records, she recruited employees from scheduling, billing and medical records to conduct the research and provide preliminary recommendations. When the practice was planning its move to a new and bigger facility, someone from each department served on the planning team.

The supervisors were sent to a two-day workshop on team building. This not only united them, but it also gave them leadership tips to help them bring out the best in their staff. Group participation increased, along with everyone's enthusiasm for the practice and their own future at Midtown Ophthalmology.

Mary then focused on strengthening the role of the Board of Directors and the communication within the leadership team. She conducted a board meeting during which physicians were asked to participate in various administrative activities. She needed one physician to be the liaison for human resources, one for finance and one for operations. The board collectively assigned these responsibilities and agreed that these responsibilities would shift to different physicians each year. Board meetings were restructured so that each department chair prepared and presented a report on the department's performance. The physicians were learning a lot about the talents and dedication of their staff.

SHARING GOALS

Mary, the physicians and the department chairs developed a strategic plan to identify goals for the following year and the actions required to achieve them. Chief among the actions were research and analysis of the practice's strengths and weaknesses. They gained a clear understanding of how they were positioned in the marketplace. At last they had a plan with concrete goals and objectives for the following year. Everyone embraced the strategic plan to help the practice achieve its objectives.

TEAM SPIRIT

Midtown Ophthalmology has a strong team, and Mary makes sure it stays that way. Staff members are recognized for their dedication and achievements. The team celebrates its successes and is proud of its accomplishments.

When the practice met the target dates for converting to a new practice management system with electronic medical records, everyone received a bottle of champagne and an afternoon off with pay. When Midtown exceeded its annual revenue goals, a luncheon was held, and everyone received a bonus. Physicians thanked the staff for their contribution and said they could not have done it without them.

Midtown Ophthalmology has annual family picnics, attended by staff, physicians and their families. They have an annual Halloween bash, with staff entertainment and prizes for best costumes. Mary implemented an Employee-Spirit award, where peers select the employee of the year. The honored employee gets two free round-trip tickets to anywhere in the continental United States. The team takes up a collection for the winner to have spending money on the trip. This isn't just a staff working together—it's a team. They support each other, encourage each other and make things happen. They have team spirit!

THE POWER OF THE TEAM

Midtown Ophthalmology presents a unified front, and there's little tolerance for divisiveness or poor performance. Everyone contributes, and the results of Team Midtown continue to astound the physicians. Some noteworthy achievements within three years of Mary coming on board as the administrator include:

- Financial performance has improved, with net per-physician revenue in the 85th percentile, based on national statistics for ophthalmology.
- The practice has received impressive patient satisfaction marks, with staff members exceeding patient expectations 95% of the time.
- The practice has achieved 100% of its annual objectives for the past two years.
- Staff members gave their supervisors an average rating of 4.5 (5 being the highest).
- Employee turnover has been less than 7% for the past two years.
- Absenteeism was reduced by 26%, and that has remained consistent.
- Overtime decreased from an average of 87 to 25 hours per month.
- The practice has exceeded referring physicians' expectations 84% of the time.

In addition to these impressive achievements, the practice grew more than 15% annually in two out of the past three years.

Unity does a lot for a practice. When everyone works well together, they are more productive and enjoy their work more. When there is leadership and goals are shared, team members take responsibility for the practice and work hard to achieve its goals.

The Secrets

1. A leader must believe in the team's potential.
2. Team building starts with the physicians.
3. Team members encourage and rely on each other.
4. The team must be acknowledged for its contribution.
5. A successful team does not tolerate poor performance.
6. Team spirit is achieved when you experience and share repeated successes.
7. Share the glory and celebrate your achievements.

FORMS ADDED TO YOUR TOOLBOX:

☞ *Physician's Retreat Questionnaire* (p. 159)
☞ *Team Leader Tips* (p. 161)

CHAPTER 7

The Dynamics of Outpatient Academic Practices

S ome of our nation's best physicians are affiliated with prestigious academic medical centers. They are conducting important research that will change the face of medicine, teaching a future generation of physicians and treating patients with rare and complicated illnesses. These physicians are vital to the practice of medicine and the future health of the world. We need them, we admire them and we find them a challenge.

> **KEY FACT:** *Performance expectations that impact the faculty practice culture must not compromise the institution's traditional academic values.*

This chapter represents a composite of outpatient clinics for different faculty practices I've worked with during my career, gathering bits of wisdom, sharing concepts, overcoming obstacles and discovering the secrets to success.

COMPETING PRIORITIES

The divergent interests and responsibilities of the academic physician result in both challenges and opportunities. These physicians are considered the cream of the crop. They are the best of the best and are sought after for their talents. They must spread their talents among four competing priorities: research, teaching, clinical patient care and administration.

A WORLD OF DIFFERENCE

In the world of medicine, the faculty practice functions differently than the private practice. Faculty practices are typically situated on large campuses in the inner city. Patients come from far and wide, and they willingly deal with the traffic, parking problems and confusion of finding the clinic. They want to see the all-knowing physician they've heard so much about. They are hoping for a treatment that will give them back a normal life. These patients are often competing for too few appointments, an unfortunate reality.

These exceptional academic physicians, unlike many physicians in private practice, don't have four days a week to devote to the outpatient clinic. Their research, teaching and administrative responsibilities can be all consuming. These divergent interests conflict with the need to accommodate clinic patients and be financially self-sustaining. Academic physicians are not accustomed to running the practice like a business, and it is not something they want to deal with. By contrast, private practice physicians understand their survival depends on turning a profit.

ADMINISTRATIVE CHALLENGES

Traditionally, the greatest source of job satisfaction for academic physicians is the recognition for academic accomplishments. Faculty physicians are absorbed in their pursuit of academic endeavors: conducting extensive research projects that will advance medicine and teaching the physicians of tomorrow. Their clinic interests and responsibilities often take a secondary position.

Typically, the academic culture focuses on the research and teaching responsibilities of faculty and does not seriously reward outpatient clinical performance. Administration must employ methods that honor and reward physicians for their clinical performance. Realistic expectations must be established and enforced. This may not be popular with academic physicians, but it is essential to the faculty practice's ability to become a self-sustaining entity, much like its peers in private practice.

Compensation plans that pay physicians based on their performance/contribution to direct patient care create an incentive for the academic physician to more fully participate. If the income distribution does not pay for performance, academic physicians will not be inclined to change their attitudes about increased participation in clinical services. The pay-for-performance compensation model is a business approach to running the outpatient clinic. This change in culture for the faculty practice must be approached in a way that does not compromise the institution's traditional academic values.

Administrative Secretaries

Academic physicians rely on administrative secretaries to assist with preparing grants, coordinate research projects, prepare teaching materials, schedule presentations and arrange travel to conferences. In addition to these responsibilities, the secretaries sometimes manage the physician's outpatient schedule, including some or all of the following:

- Receive incoming patient phone calls;
- Schedule clinic patients (by phone);
- Pull the physician's charts for the clinic session;
- Prepare the charge tickets;
- Collect completed charge tickets;
- Sort mail; and
- File.

These tasks are an adjunct to the important research and teaching support the secretaries give their physicians. For this reason, the secretaries interest in the clinic is limited. They do not actually work in the clinic and are unable to relate to or take responsibility for the clinic's efficiency, patient flow or demands on the outpatient staff. This remote service can unknowingly compromise physician productivity, patient satisfaction, clinic efficiency and profitability. When these tasks are performed by a dedicated staff that works in the clinic, efficiency in patient services and workflow is achieved, resulting in improved physician productivity and greater patient satisfaction. Removing these responsibilities from the secretaries requires a change in mindset. Because the physicians are accustomed to relying on secretaries that understand their needs and look out for their interests, they may be reluctant to make this transition.

Centralization

The business side of academic medicine has moved to the forefront with the appearance of managed care and reduced reimbursement. Major teaching hospitals have developed centralized administrative organizations to address the business and economic needs of the academic faculty practice. These organizations have a variety of names and associated acronyms such as: management service organization (MSO), centralized business office (CBO) and management business office (MBO). Their primary purpose is to assume responsibility for administrative services to increase operational efficiency and improve financial performance of the faculty practice.

When business functions are provided by centralized services, administration monitors and reports on the performance of the outpatient clinic, something the physicians are not accustomed to. If finances are scrutinized and productivity expectations emerge, physicians resist, making it difficult to obtain the cooperation essential to improving productivity, efficiency and finances.

The implementation of centralized administrative services generally begins with assuming responsibility for managing clinic revenue and expenses, including the billing and collections processes. Once this is successful, other functions are delegated to centralized administration, such as handling incoming phone calls, scheduling and staffing the clinic. Physicians may resist these changes for fear more expectations will be put upon them, a potential threat to their academic interests.

Physicians must be convinced that centralizing clinic functions offers substantial benefits to them and will not add burdens to already-demanding work schedules. This can be accomplished if the physicians share management's objectives, and they work together to achieve them. The physicians must believe that there is a valid need to move the clinic in a new direction, their interests are protected and the gains are worth the effort. This requires an evaluation of the outpatient clinic's performance.

The clinic assessment provides detailed objective findings that are data-driven and compared with a valid benchmark. This is best achieved by selecting someone outside the organization to conduct the study. An independent consulting team has no political agenda or bias to cloud its opinions. When sound analysis and recommendations are presented, academic physicians are less resistant. If administration is willing to be measured by the same yardstick, this becomes even more convincing. The performance report card then becomes the physicians' baseline to compare the administrations' future performance when centralized services are implemented.

OPERATIONAL ASSESSMENT

The success of the operational assessment requires a clear understanding of the organizational culture, structure, leadership, communication and decision-making processes. The project objectives and related concerns must be clearly defined and agreed upon. The final report is expected to provide recommendations that support any or all of these organizational objectives:
1. Strengthen communication;

2. Develop shared objectives;
3. Improve operating performance;
4. Standardize patient services;
5. Increase patient satisfaction;
6. Improve financial performance; and
7. Attain self-sustaining financial position.

The influence and value of the report are directly related to a clear rationale for each recommendation and identifying the associated risks, opportunities and economic impact. A Risk Opportunity Matrix is an effective visual tool to assist in accomplishing this. If the argument for change is not compelling, it will be difficult to obtain the desired commitment.

CLINIC PERFORMANCE

Conducting an analysis of the faculty practice is an arduous process that includes:

- Collecting relevant documents and historical data;
- Preparing and distributing survey instruments;
- Conducting interviews;
- Examining comparative secondary data;
- Performing the on-site review; and
- Developing and presenting the report.

The assessment focuses on the typical operational systems involved with patient services—from the initial phone call and scheduling the appointment to the completion of the patient encounter. The consultants will take a critical look at access, staffing, productivity and customer service to determine:

- How patient services can be improved?
- What duplication or redundant processes exist?
- If resources are being optimized?
- How productivity can be increased?

Access

Access often emerges as one of the major issues that must be addressed in the faculty practice. Patients frequently complain about the length of time they wait to be seen. The wait for a new patient visit in some specialties exceeds 30 days, and a return patient is likely to wait 20 days or more. Instead of waiting for an appointment, patients sometimes go elsewhere, creating a missed opportunity for the practice. Exploring the reason for poor access and the effect it has on patient satisfaction and financial performance is paramount to understanding what actions should be taken.

Productivity and Managing the Scheduling System

Addressing access issues and physician productivity begins with managing the entire scheduling system, not just the scheduling of patients. The outpatient scheduling system should maximize the facility by deploying the appropriate number of physicians for every clinic session. Simply put, if each physician needs to toggle between 3 exam rooms and there are 15 exam rooms in the clinic, five physicians should be scheduled to work in the clinic every session. In my experience, this is not a reality, nor is it given importance.

Academic physicians are scheduled to work in the outpatient clinics when it does not compromise their competing priorities of teaching, research and administration. The availability to conduct clinic sessions is constantly changing as research grants are sought, research projects ensue, conferences are scheduled and the physicians' teaching responsibilities shift throughout the year. While it certainly doesn't happen in every faculty practice, it is nonetheless not uncommon for physicians to cancel clinic sessions for weeks, even months at a time. If other physicians are not assigned to fill the vacant slots, clinic space, physician productivity and patient access suffer.

In reality, an already pent-up demand for patient access increases, revenue declines and customer service plummets when physicians cancel their sessions. For the most part, management either skirts this issue or has been unsuccessful in developing collaborative efforts with physicians to overcome this looming problem. Expectations and standards are not applied for maintaining scheduled sessions. No limit has been established for the number of sessions that may be canceled. This leaves the clinic with an unmanaged scheduling system that does not match supply with demand. In the overall scheme, this represents a substantial loss in revenue, when expenses remain consistent.

In some instances, the scheduling system is further compromised because there simply aren't enough physicians to meet the demand. If the physical capacity can accommodate additional providers, the use of mid-level extenders proves to be an excellent way to fill vacant sessions and improve access, as long as the physicians and management support this concept.

Other complications that contribute to an unmanaged scheduling system are physicians that move their sessions to a more convenient day, without particular concern for the availability of space or the imposition to patients or support staff. They may arrive at the clinic with a full schedule only to discover they are competing for exam rooms. These physicians are now waiting for exam rooms with their patients backing up. This happens because too many doctors are vying for too few exam rooms. Yet, there are other days when the clinic space is under-utilized because physicians have cancelled their sessions. A well managed scheduling system that optimizes space results in reduced frustration for physicians and patients, and improves the clinic's financial position.

Optimizing Clinical Sessions

The economics of optimizing clinical space can be explored by developing the maximum revenue projections, built from internal assumptions that consider pre-determined average revenue per patient and multiply this number by the maximum number of patients that can be accommodated in the facility.

Example: Let's assume the outpatient clinic can accommodate five physicians in sessions simultaneously, and each half-day session consists of three hours. If the physician-scheduling template accommodates three patients per hour, the maximum number of patients that could be seen in one physician's session would be nine. We'll use a modest figure of $125.00 for the average revenue per patient visit.

$$5 \text{ MDs} \times 2 \text{ sessions/day} = 10 \text{ sessions/day}$$
$$3 \text{ patient visits/hour} \times 3 \text{ hours/session} = 9$$
$$\text{Average revenue/patient visit} = \$125$$
$$10 \times 9 \times \$125 = \$11{,}250 \text{ daily revenue}$$

When this number is multiplied by five days a week and 50 weeks a year (eliminating an estimated two weeks a year when the clinic is closed for holidays), the total annual revenue in this example would be $2,812,500, for an allocation of five full-time-equivalent physicians to serve the clinic.

Another factor that influences the ability to optimize the clinic and obtain an improved financial outcome is missed appointments—the no shows and late cancellations that are not filled. In my experience, it is not uncommon for faculty practices to have a missed appointment rate between 24% and

38%. This occurs at the same time patients calling for appointments are required to wait an unrealistic amount of time to see a physician, because "the schedule is full." Faculty practices must consider these missed appointments as substantial lost revenue and a deterent to patient satisfaction.

Missed appointments also result in increased overhead related to staff time involved with the intended patient visit. The employee activities required for each scheduled appointment include taking the initial phone call, scheduling the appointment, locating and preparing the chart, reviewing demographics, preparing a charge ticket, documenting the no show, calling the patient to reschedule and returning the chart to the file system. These steps have all been taken for a visit that does not take place and does not generate revenue for the practice. It is realistic to assume this has taken an average of 15 minutes per patient for an estimated $6 in staffing costs. If the clinic experiences 10 no shows a day, it has absorbed staffing overhead of more than $14,000 a year that will not be offset by revenue. Add to this the lost physician productivity and allocating clinical resources and space based on scheduled patients, and the economics of the missed appointment are dismal.

Missed appointments also restrict other patients' ability to obtain an appointment in a clinic where the demand often exceeds access. In other words, patients are vying to get into the clinic at the same time there are holes in the schedule, because of no shows and late cancellations. Improving access so that patients can be seen in the clinic sooner contributes to a reduction in missed appointments. Results are further improved when an effective appointment-confirmation system is in place.

Building a well-managed scheduling system dramatically improves physician productivity, patient access and profitability. In order to accomplish this, systems and processes must be in place to accommodate the increased productivity. This is where centralization becomes the clinic's ally. If some of the responsibilities for running the clinic are shifted to centralized services, information and needs will be better managed, and the remaining activities of running the outpatient facility can be given the attention that is needed to serve the patients better.

Staffing

Shifting responsibilities related to the clinic from the physician's secretary to clinic staff will succeed with proper planning and clear delineation of duties. Removing these duties from the secretaries allows them to focus on academic endeavors. When clinical staff members assume the clinic-related duties, it promotes increased efficiency, improved outcome and better control. It is important that staff resources be properly allocated to ensure the workload is evenly distributed.

When positions are designed by area of specialty (i.e., scheduling, phone coverage, medical records, patient registration), individuals are more likely to become "experts" at their job—rather than jacks-of-all-trades, but mastering none. Specialization increases staff confidence and improves performance. This does not mean employees should not be cross-trained. By all means, this is important to smooth patient flow and support their co-workers. When the workload is well distributed and the staff is confident and capable, functional work teams develop. Members of the work teams respect each other's contribution and learn to depend on each other, which results in better patient services.

Developing well-defined job descriptions helps clarify the duties each person will perform and lists the primary responsibilities for the position. The job description should also describe the qualifications of the position—education, skills and experience. The job description must also describe the physical demands of the position, as required by the Americans with Disabilities Act. In addition to listing the major tasks under the job responsibilities, it is advisable to include a final line item "and other duties as assigned." This discourages the "it's not in my job description" attitude.

The organization's objectives and mission can be reinforced by establishing performance standards that support these. Let's say one of the objectives is to be more patient-focused. If the staff is expected to be courteous and helpful to patients in support of this objective, you may want a standard for the receptionist that states patients will be greeted with a smile and by name within 30 seconds of their arrival. Further state that this expectation must be met 95% of the time. Of course, the performance must then be monitored to be sure the employee meets the expectation.

E-fficiency

Most faculty practices lead the way in implementing technology to improve operational efficiency. Physicians and staff are hooked up to the Internet and intranets. Unfortunately, many people are not making the leap to use the computer to expedite and improve communication. Interoffice e-mail and instant messaging need to replace getting up from a workstation to talk to someone or using the telephone.

Many clinics have moved toward electronic health records (EHR), commonly referred to as electronic medical records (EMRs). Some of these practices still hold on to the hard copy of the patient's chart. If the EHR software has the capability to eliminate the hard copy record, steps should be taken to accomplish this.

Hand-held computers are instrumental in helping physicians' access information, report their charges and reduce the time involved with these tasks. This contributes to timely and accurate charge entry, reduces the potential for dropping charges, eliminates concern about misplaced charge tickets and saves staff time. The software is generally user-friendly, reducing problems inherent with the learning curve.

E-scribing has been particularly helpful in managing patient prescriptions and saving time. When this is tied to the EMR, functions are enhanced, and the timesavings can be substantial.

Patients can add to the clinic's efficiency when they are Internet savvy and the faculty practice has expanded its technology to include patient participation. Patients can go to the website to learn more about the faculty practice and the scope of services that are offered. They can obtain maps that reduce the need to obtain oral directions to the facility. Many medical organizations have implemented technology that allows patients to pre-register and schedule appointments online. These various features promote efficiency, improve communication and service and contribute to cost containment. Once a website is patient-friendly and able to improve patient services, the staff must be trained to direct patients to the website.

CUSTOMER SERVICE

Customer service in the medical facility is measured by patient satisfaction, and how satisfied the patient is in the academic setting is questionable. It begins with poor access, as previously discussed, but moves beyond that to an attitude that can permeate the clinic. Physicians may have an attitude of superiority that patients can sense. Support staff, on the other hand, may take a come-what-may attitude; "I'm just doing my job; this is the way it is, and there's nothing I can do about it."

These attitudes are damaging to the reputation of the academic practice and result in patient dissatisfaction. Patients already have to deal with frustration in waiting for an appointment, driving out of their own community, difficulty with parking and meandering through a large campus to find the outpatient clinic where they are scheduled. Add to this that the person greeting them is perfunctory with no interest in or sensitivity to the patients' situation, and patients are bound to be discontented.

Conducting Surveys

Customer service reports in faculty practices may be skewed by the methodology employed to measure patient satisfaction. Often the surveys are completed and collected at the clinic. This survey technique can result in the same individual repeatedly responding to the survey. It also limits the sampling to voluntary participation. This creates an inability to know if the sampling is representative of the clinic population served. The survey results become biased, unreliable and useless.

It is suggested that patient satisfaction surveys be conducted and analyzed by a professional surveyor, unrelated to the organization. Although this requires an investment, it is essential to obtaining and analyzing quantitative information that is reliable. Once baseline results are acquired, the practice can establish defined improvement goals.

Dispute Resolution

Developing standardized dispute-resolution processes offers an opportunity to obtain qualitative information about patients' complaints. An incident report needs to be completed with each dispute. The report should describe the complaint and the measures taken to resolve it. When a control copy is kept on file, the clinic can review the issues that emerged, the action taken, which staff member handled the situation and the time frame required to take corrective action. To improve efficiency and save time, the documentation processes can be automated. By reviewing trends over time, an internal report card emerges. This gives the clinic the opportunity to examine its own commitment to customer satisfaction.

The Commitment

A commitment to patient satisfaction and customer service does not happen overnight, and it is not the result of a workshop or a trendy customer service byline. A commitment to patient satisfaction must be demonstrated at the top. Seeing patients on time, being approachable and listening to their needs goes a long way in achieving patient satisfaction. Support staff will take their lead from the physicians, but must be held to a standard that treats patients with dignity and respect. When patient satisfaction is woven into the performance review, support staff will take notice.

Patients are attracted to the academic medical center because of its reputation as a leading innovative medical research and teaching institution. It's important that the patient believes the physicians are approachable and the clinic is a "caring" place.

BUILDING TRUST

Cultural, economic and operational changes cannot be accomplished without a foundation of trust. The ingredients for trust are grounded in our behavior, personal integrity and respect. Obtaining a commitment and cooperation is dependent on listening and responding to the other person's needs and objections. Trust is gained when those commitments are honored and both parties are working toward a mutual goal.

FACING CHANGE

It's a bold step forward to face change head-on, knowing it takes us to places unknown. Just the same, unless we are willing to examine what has changed in and around us, and look at the implications, we will not be able to progress and make the most of the future. This is true whether you are a revered academic physician, a computer analyst, administrator, supervisor, medical assistant or file clerk.

Many academic faculty practices have the advantage of skilled administrators focused on helping them succeed in a changing environment. Once the relationship is grounded with trust, physicians and administration have an opportunity to create a new, dynamic performance model – one that relates to physicians' needs, business essentials and customer service. Times are changing, and we all must adjust in order to progress and be a part of the future.

There are a few things that are paramount to the ability to accept and endorse change. Each person must:
1. Believe the change is for the better and the outcome is worth the effort;
2. Be flexible enough to adapt to change; and
3. Contribute to achieving the desired result.

If we do not contribute to the change process, we may, directly or indirectly, sabotage the results. Sabotage is not unfamiliar to the change agent, and it is often a result of suspicious attitudes, inflexibility or arrogance. It is overcome when everyone involved in an effort pulls together to accomplish a goal. This is certainly more difficult to achieve in large academic practices, where employees sometimes lack a strong commitment to the organization. Management must make every effort to build relationships with line staff members that will contribute to staff's sense of belonging and increase their commitment.

TAKING ACTION

The operational assessment is a call to action. As such, administration and physicians are wise to agree beforehand on how they will respond to the report. The report should not be used as a political weapon where people are compelled to defend their position on issues or discount the value of the report when they oppose its findings. It is important to regard the report as a valid, objective review of the faculty practice operations. The report's constructive criticism and recommendations are designed to provide a blueprint for the faculty practice to achieve its stated goals.

The operational study is an opportunity for the faculty practice to set its course in a new direction. The report becomes the basis for working collaboratively, as long as each party is flexible and focuses on improving operational performance, patient services and financial outcomes. This can be accomplished when each stakeholder understands this, seeks the same result and is willing to do what is necessary to achieve it. Academic physicians entrenched in their career advancement are not accustomed to this type of collaboration. Without these cooperative efforts, the future of academic medical centers is threatened. The message is clear: set special interests aside, put down the armor and work for the greater good of the organization.

The Secrets

1. Acknowledge the competing priorities of academic physicians.
2. Remove clinic-related tasks from the administrative secretaries' responsibilities.
3. Pay-for-performance compensation plans will increase the academic physician's commitment to the outpatient clinic.

4. Centralized services are designed to improve the clinic's performance.
5. Academic faculty practices must be self-sustaining without compromising physicians' academic pursuits.
6. Optimizing clinical space is critical to improving clinic productivity and enhancing revenue.
7. An unbiased operational assessment provides a blueprint to meet the academic faculty practice's goals.
8. A commitment to patient satisfaction begins at the top.
9. Trust is critical to building collaborative working relationships.
10. Build accountability into the system to get results.

FORMS ADDED TO YOUR TOOLBOX:

☞ *Risk/Opportunity Matrix* (p. 162)
☞ *Sample Performance Standards Worksheet* (p. 163)

CHAPTER 8

The Power of Revenue Management

Revenue management is multifaceted, and, as with every area of practice performance, the greater the commitment the greater the result. It takes an organized approach that starts before patients select their physician and ends with the final payment.

Getting paid for what you do remains one of the biggest concerns for physicians and administrators across the country. This concern exists for academic practices, group practices (both small and large) and solo physicians. There's not one big secret, but there are many little secrets and actions that are worthy of administrator and physician attention to improve revenue performance.

> **KEY FACT:** *Getting paid more for what you do depends on a multitude of decisions and begins before the patient is seen.*

CAPTURING CHARGES

When I ask physicians to describe the process of capturing charges, they tell me it's a matter of documenting all the services on the office or hospital charge ticket and being sure the charges are entered into the billing system. These are vital processes to capturing charges, but there are other factors that play an important role in increasing revenue by capturing more charges. It begins with contracting.

Contracting Issues

There are physicians that do their own contracting and those that delegate some or all of this responsibility to managed care organizations (MCO) through a centralized management service organization or independent provider association. Physicians that have relinquished the control of contracting to a third party have done so because of convenience, fear or concern about the ability to obtain the best contract terms on their own. These third parties may or may not be effective at representing physicians and obtaining favorable fee schedules or payment terms. Furthermore, they sometimes fail to provide the practice with copies of the contracts and associated fee schedules.

It's the responsibility of the practice to evaluate and monitor the performance of the third-party payers and hold them to the terms of the contract. I am amazed by how many times I've encountered a practice that either does not have copies of contracts and related fee schedules or has them but does not know where they are. How can such a practice be sure it is getting paid correctly and that the terms of the contract are not being violated? Physicians and staff cannot enforce the contract and have no means to hold the payer accountable unless they have a copy of the contract and its supporting documents.

Take a critical look at the insurance companies you contract with or intend to contract with in the future. Just because a new payer arrives on the scene, it doesn't mean you need to jump on board and obtain a contract. Look at the potential impact before you sign on. Does this insurance company or MCO have a contract with an important employer in town? Will further physician referrals be jeopardized if you don't sign on? What are the implications to the practice if you do or don't sign on?

Physicians have allowed insurance plans to dictate fees and terms of contracts in the past, but that doesn't mean they need to in the future. It's time to take back the control. Scrutinize every contract you are considering. Don't let the emotions of the situation get the best of you, even if the insurance company appears to be a major player in town.

Fees are negotiable. Ask to see the plan's fees for the top 10–20 codes utilized by the practice—and don't sign the contract otherwise. Financial vulnerability and potential risk exist in not knowing how much you will be paid and when. If you don't ask for more, you're not going to get it, and it must be done before signing the contract!

Don't assume that you are locked into the terms of some boilerplate contract that's being passed around to all the doctors in town. Learn to say no to terms that aren't acceptable. For example, a contract may require a physician to submit claims within 60 days of service, but may not specify a time limit on when the payer actually pays the physician. Why would a physician agree to those terms? Of course, there is some protection if your state has legislation that requires the insurance plan to pay claims within a certain number of days. Check with your state's Prompt Payment Laws before you agree to a contract that does not specify payment terms.

Keep in mind that the relevant documents mentioned in the contract, not just the contract itself, should be examined. Physicians need a clear understanding of the grievance process from the start, not once a problem emerges. Review the plan's quality assurance and utilization management procedures. Find out what the plan expects from the practice and what the practice will be agreeing to once the contract is finalized. What are the call- coverage requirements? Also get a clear understanding of the medical liability the practice will own under the contract. Does it include a hold-harmless clause to protect the physicians and the practice? It's wise to have the contract reviewed by your malpractice carrier and/or lawyer in advance. *The practice must protect its own interests!*

Turn to professional organizations for guidance in reviewing contracts. The Professional Association of Health Care Office Management (PAHCOM), Medical Group Management Association (MGMA), state medical associations and specialty societies have tools to help medical practices examine and understand an insurance contract and its implications.

Keep Staff Informed

Once the contract has been signed, someone in the office must assume responsibility for educating the staff about the essentials. Make sure you have the answers to these questions *before* patients arrive in the office:

1. Are all the physicians/providers contracted with the plan?
2. What are the data collection requirements?
3. Is pre-authorization required, and if so, are services limited to consultation or are diagnostic studies and follow-up included in the authorization?
4. Can benefits verification, eligibility, pre-authorization and the referral process be handled through the Internet?
5. What are the patient's responsibilities, and, if the patient fails to meet these responsibilities, what action is the practice permitted to take?
6. What services are NOT covered by the contract?
7. For noncovered services, can payment be collected from the patient when the services are rendered, or is the practice required to submit a claim that is denied by the payer before it can collect from the patient?

8. What are the billing requirements, including time limits, where claims are submitted and if substantiating documents are required?
9. Who is the plan's provider-relations contact for the office, and what is that person's direct phone number?
10. What happens if the plan becomes insolvent?
11. What is the fee schedule?

Too often, staff members don't have a copy of the fee schedule for the plan. If your billing department assumes the practice is being paid correctly and post the payment and adjustment accordingly, it may be absorbing losses for underpayments. This can cost the practice many thousands of dollars each month. I've seen it happen all too often. Remember: A well-informed staff guards the practice's financial interest.

Patient Registration

There's power in the patient registration process. Respect it! The patient registration form is the patient's first financial document in the practice and is vital for making sure the practice gets paid. The form must be user-friendly. Use words the patients recognize. If patients are complaining about completing or updating the form and ask questions that demonstrate confusion, redesign the form. Make sure the form is system-friendly, too. Because staff members are accustomed to viewing the registration information on screen, they can quickly spot missing data if the patient registration form simulates the computer registration screen. This will result in a faster and more accurate registration process.

Educate, enforce and reinforce the importance of patient registration. This means holding staff and patients accountable. The staff must take responsibility for obtaining accurate patient registration information *at each visit*. Patients must do their part by providing you with the information. There are important questions to ask established patients at each visit. Keeping patient registration information current depends on how these questions are asked. There's a right way and a wrong way (Table 1).

This matrix should be part of the staff training and remain the mantra for keeping insurance information current at each visit. If there are changes, input them in the computer system when the questions are asked—and get an updated copy of the patient's insurance card. Working in "real-time" ensures accuracy. The billing office, nurses and doctors can pull up the

TABLE 1. Right and Wrong Ways to Ask for Patient Information

Information Needed	Right Way	Wrong Way
Current phone number	Please confirm your home and work phone numbers for me.	Are your phone numbers the same?
Current address	Mrs. Smith, are you still living at 312 Windy Drive?	Mrs. Smith, is your address the same?
Employer	Are you still employed by the City of New York?	Have you changed jobs?
Insurance	Is Aetna Preferred still your primary insurance?	Do you still have the same primary and secondary insurance?
Insurance	Do you have secondary insurance coverage with United Healthcare?	
Insurance	Is this visit due to a workers' compensation or auto injury?	Not asking about the possibility of injury.

patient's account or electronic medical record and have the most accurate demographic information.

CHARGE REPORTING

The charge ticket should be reviewed annually. Are all the codes updated to comply with the latest versions of both CPT and ICD-9 codes? Does it make sense, is it multifunctional? Does it contribute to ease in documenting the visit, data entry, scheduling follow-up care and collecting payment? Too often, charge tickets have detailed printed information that serves little purpose in documenting the encounter. Here are a few suggestions in designing a functional form:

- Patient demographics and insurance information should appear at the top of the form.
- List only the top office CPT codes, based on actual utilization. Utilization data can be pulled from the computer system for the past 12 months to guide this process.

- Do not place hospital services on the office charge ticket.
- List only the top diagnostic (ICD-9) codes, based on utilization.
- Leave a space for staff instructions (i.e., what diagnostic studies need to be scheduled and when the patient needs to return to the office).
- Designate an area to document the payment received and the balance on the account.

Many of these suggestions apply to creating a hospital charge ticket. Simple to use, functional charge tickets make it easy to document activity, improving the ability to capture charges and obtain relevant data.

When it comes to reporting hospital charges, many physicians fall short by not completing the charge document in real-time. This can be a major contributor to inaccurate coding, lost charges, duplication of effort, staff inefficiency and delayed billing. I once worked with a gastroenterology practice that failed to charge for 15% of its hospital procedures, a total of more than $100,000 a year, because the physicians failed to report these procedures to the billing department.

Accurate and timely charge submission is the responsibility of the person performing the service. Providers should not be delegating this function to someone else in the office.

Many practices are implementing automated charge reporting, an excellent method to document and capture charges that improves efficiency and accuracy. If you are considering electronic charge reporting, plan ahead. Obtain input from physicians, nurses, data entry and billing to ensure that the electronic system meets the needs of the entire practice, saves time and results in optimizing charge capture activities. By all means, it's important not to skimp on training. Allowing time to be properly trained on the system will reduce frustration, save time and ensure that you are making the most of the systems capabilities.

Coding Accuracy

Every practice needs a resident coding expert on staff. The coding expert examines charge activity to be sure visits are coded properly (both ICD-9 and CPT, including modifiers). Empower your coder to assume responsibility for educating physicians and staff. When you find inaccurate charge tickets, use them as examples to conduct a coding review for physicians and staff so the coding errors are not repeated.

REVENUE RECOVERY

Once the practice has taken the appropriate steps in capturing and reporting charges, the revenue-recovery process begins, and the actions taken can either improve or impede cash flow. If claims are accurate with timely submission, it will result in improved cash flow. Incomplete claims or inaccurate payments result in duplication of efforts. inefficiency and a slowdown in payment. This increases practice expenses at the same time revenue is being delayed. Quality claims submission remains paramount to improved revenue-recovery processes.

Set revenue-recovery standards in the office. Establish what you consider to be reasonable and acceptable. Provide the tools and support necessary to meet these guidelines, and then hold staff accountable based on the standards. Here are some examples:

- **Accurate claims submission:** This can be measured by the number of claims that are rejected by your clearinghouse or insurance plans. Determine an acceptable error ratio, but keep the standard high (i.e., less than 3%–5%). Errors can be traced and used for staff education and accountability. For example, if the patient's date of birth or insurance plan numbers cannot be identified, an error has been made in collecting the data or entering it into the system. Also establish a turnaround standard such as a rejected claim must be properly resubmitted as a clean claim within 72 hours, and exceptions must be justified. With electronic charge reporting, these time frames can be reduced.
- **Timely claims submission:**

▪ Charge entry	Office:	1 to 2 days
	Inpatient:	2 to 5 days
	Surgery:	2 to 5 days
▪ Billing submission	Office:	5 to 7 days
	Inpatient:	7 to 10 days
	Surgery:	7 to 10 days

- **Timely claims payment:** If claims are submitted accurately, payment should reach the office within 30 to 45 days.
- **Accurate and timely patient billing:**
  - ▪ Once a claim is paid by the insurance company and the required contract adjustment is made, the balance should be transferred to patient responsibility immediately.

- Patient statements should be generated within 30 days of transferring to patient responsibility. The timeliest method to accomplish prompt billing is cycle billing: separating the patient accounts into four alphabetical batches and billing each batch during a different week of the month. This also spreads out patient calls to the billing department regarding statements.
- Co-pays must be paid at the time of service.
- Patient balances should be collected:
  — If and when the patient returns to the office; or
  — Within 30 days of the patient receiving a statement.

Practices that fail to establish written revenue-recovery standards are jeopardizing the ability to improve cash flow and optimize revenue.

MONITORING PERFORMANCE

The power of revenue management includes monitoring internal and external performance—what physicians, staff, patients, MCOs and insurance plans are doing that impact revenue and whether intervention is required.

Conducting Chart Audits

One of the most effective ways to analyze performance with charge reporting and payer payments is the chart audit. Conducting audits is also a key component to an effective compliance program. Practices can implement their own procedures to accomplish this, but will be most effective when they involve physicians and staff. If teams are formed with a receptionist or scheduler, nurse, physician and someone from the billing department, the cross representation and broader knowledge result in a better audit. It also serves as an educational process and greater understanding of everyone's contribution to revenue management. The resident coder or your compliance officer should serve as the project manager.

Pull five to 10 random charts for each physician and mid-level provider to obtain a broad range of patient types, services and payers. For each patient, select one day's encounter, going back at least eight weeks prior to the date of the audit. For each selected encounter, additional information must be collected:

- Appointment record;
- Chart notes;
- Charge ticket;

- Patient ledger (itemization of charges, adjustments and payments); and
- Explanation of benefits (EOB).

Carefully review and compare each document looking for any discrepancies. The appointment record and chart note should match dates and patient name. If the chart belongs to John T. Smith and the documentation states the encounter took place on April 3, be sure John T. Smith appears on the appointment schedule, not John A. Smith, an entirely different patient. Such a discrepancy would require further research to correct.

The documentation on the chart notes must validate the services appearing on the charge ticket including date of service, diagnosis and procedure codes for the visit and other ancillary services. Review the chart and verify that reports are in the file and that they have been read and signed off on by the physician.

The charges on the charge ticket should mirror charges appearing on the patient ledger. This audit process confirms that no data entry errors were made and no charges were missed.

The final step is a review of the EOB to verify that the insurance plan processed the claim and reimbursed for the services properly. Insurance companies make errors—make it your responsibility to find them. Errors in adjudicating claims should be caught by the billing department when posting the payment, but your audit will serve as a double check and reinforce accountability.

If errors are detected during the audit, estimate the cost to the practice. If the audit reveals a potential gain of 12% on evaluation and management (E&M) services, calculate this against the revenue for those procedures over the past year. For example, if E&M office codes represented $265,000 of last year's revenue, an additional 12% would be nearly $32,000. That's not small change!

The first chart audit becomes the baseline for improving performance and educating both providers and staff. Periodic audits should be built into your system to measure progress and ensure compliance.

If an internal audit results in substantial errors throughout the various departments, it may be best to bring in a coding and reimbursement specialist to train staff and implement effective revenue management policies and procedures. Don't be shortsighted by focusing on the costs to accomplish this—the investment can pay big dividends.

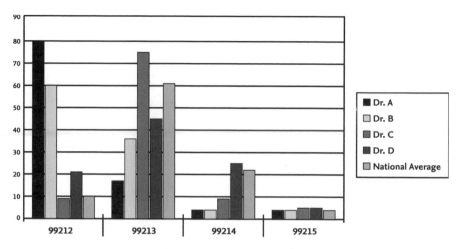

FIGURE 1. Physician charge patterns analysis. E&M coding: internal medicine.

Coding Patterns

Examine and compare the E&M coding patterns of the physicians by pulling the top 10 encounter codes for both hospital and office visits. Compare this with the national utilization of E&M codes, available through the MGMA or Medicare, which publishes E&M coding statistics by specialty. The MGMA provides broader and more meaningful numbers, because its reports include various patient age groups, not just Medicare patients. These reports also break down key CPT codes by diagnosis, which enables the practice to dig deeper into coding practices (Figure 1).

This peer-review process proves helpful in identifying physicians that may be too aggressive or too cautious in the way they apply E&M codes and whether the group may be incurring risk exposure as a result of a physician's coding practices. At the same time, if one physician seems to be on the mark with proper coding, she can help other physicians extend their knowledge of coding application.

Identifying the Poor-Performing Payer

The practice administrator takes the lead role in looking out for the practice's interests when dealing with insurance plans or MCOs. It is prudent to implement procedures to monitor payer performance and decide which insurance plans should be continued or truncated. Maybe it's time to identify the bottom-feeders and cancel those managed care contracts that are more trouble than they are worth. This strategy has merit, but requires analysis to identify which payers are the culprits that wreak havoc on the practice, and whether it makes sense to eliminate them. Use the following as a guide:

1. **Examine the hassle factor.** The manager and insurance biller will need to examine key indicators and past performance patterns of third-party payers. A look at these four key indicators will identify the payers that give the most hassle:

   • *The plan requires repeated requests for referral or authorization:* Look for the payers (insurance plans or MCOs) that physicians and staff struggle with or that require excessive time to deal with.

   • *Slow claims processing:* If there are payers that repeatedly reject clean claims or ask for information that has already been provided or is not necessary to process the claim, put these payers on the hassle list.

   • *Patients complain about their insurance company:* When patients come to a physician or staff member complaining about poor service from their insurance company, listen. This can be a sign of trouble. The payer may be cutting staff because it cannot meet its bottom line. On the other hand, it may not have invested in the infrastructure required to support its members and maintain viability.

   • *Provider-relations support is substandard:* If staff members are frustrated with the lack of support they receive from provider relations or the inability to get their questions answered, the payer may be more trouble than it is worth.

   Rate each payer, giving it one point for each "yes" it receives on the above hassle factors. A zero rating represents a premier payer in terms of the hassle factor.

2. **Review the outstanding claims reports.** For several months in a row, generate and review the outstanding claims reports. This will identify the payers that account for the highest volume of outstanding claims and those that account for the largest amount of revenue due on outstanding claims. The top five may be the same or may be varied. If, for example, one payer appears each month that accounts for a high volume of claims, but not a major amount of revenue, you may want to act on it. Canceling this contract may not have significant financial repercussions, but might save valuable staff time. However, before determining this, check out the referring source for these patients. If it turns out

to be an important referring physician, discuss the situation with him before you act. Communicating up front can reduce the chances of alienating referring physicians.

3. **Assess reimbursement rates.** Based on the top 10 CPT codes utilization for the practice, develop a spreadsheet on payer performance. This will identify the variable payments of different plans and reveal the poorer-paying contracts.

When the troublesome payers have been identified, assess the potential impact of eliminating any or all of these payers. Measure this impact with the following points in mind:

- Volume of business the payer represents;
- Impact on existing and potential patients;
- Loss of revenue and long-term economic effect;
- Existing scheduling needs (perhaps eliminating a few payers will open up time on the schedule to see more patients from other better-paying sources); and
- Political issues that may exist with referring physicians (perhaps they are considering dropping a poor payer or feel compelled to provide service to a poor payer for reasons that are unknown to you).

If you decide to fire some of the payers, drop the worst payer first and measure the impact. Begin by reviewing the existing contract to be sure the terms required for termination are not violated. Decide how to communicate your intention to drop the plan to referring physicians and patients who are members of the plan. It will be important to continue providing care for plan patients under treatment. Be sure no one in the practice makes negative comments about the payer to patients or other practices. It serves no purpose and takes away from the professionalism of the practice.

Even if your analysis results in a decision not to fire any existing payers, examining these key indicators provides a basis to monitor payer performance over time. It also puts the practice in a knowing position that holds payers accountable to meet specific expectations.

Office Collections

Collecting from patients when they are in the office is referred to as over-the-counter (OTC) payment. Effective OTC collection requires staff members to assume responsibility for collecting patient payments whenever patients have an appointment.

Failure to collect from patients is a missed opportunity, resulting in delayed payment and further expense. Some experts estimate a cost of $12 to $15 to send a patient a statement. With $15 co-pays, you just break even, and that's assuming the patient pays with the first statement.

It's more important than ever to establish policies and procedures for OTC payments, as employers shift more financial responsibility for medical care to patients through larger deductibles and co-pays, and for a greater portion of the medical services they receive. This means if the practice doesn't implement tight collection procedures, it is likely to end up with a rising accounts receivable (A/R). Receptionists at both the receiving and exit stations should be trained in and held accountable for collecting from patients—both co-pays and existing patient balances.

Increased accountability is best accomplished when the batch of daily charge tickets is reviewed, comparing OTC payments with the amount patients actually owed. Establish OTC collection goals, and review them with the receptionists. If they have difficulty asking for money, they can observe another staffer that excels in this area. They can also do some role playing. I once worked with a four-physician urology practice that doubled OTC payments within 30 days once staff was trained. The physicians were impressed as the receptionists continued to increase the amount they collected. The doctors complimented the receptionists on their progress. This was enough motivation to keep the staff confident and focused on raising the bar. Just think of how much time and money were saved by not having to send out repeated statements and reducing the amount of time staff spent following up on patient balances.

The most effective way to achieve the target OTC collection goal is to establish graduated expectations for improvement over a specific period of time (Table 2).

Each week, monitor staff members' performance with OTC payments, and share the results with them. Continue to encourage and praise them as they progress. Some practices offer bonuses when targets are hit, as an incentive to improve collections.

If staff members struggle to hit the targets, provide additional support to teach them the skills necessary to obtain patient payments and overcome obstacles that prevent this. At the same time, recognize that not every employee is right for this position. Some people just can't get comfortable

TABLE 2. OTC Collection Goals

OTC Payments	Average Daily OTC Collections	Payment as a % of Patients' Balances	Percentage of Patients That Paid the Visit Co-Pay
Historical performance	$406	12	55
30-day target		50	80
60-day target		70	100
90-day target		90	100

OTC = over-the-counter.

asking patients for money. Know when you need to shift a different person into the position before someone feels inadequate or thinks he has failed.

ACCOUNTS RECEIVABLE MANAGEMENT

Examine A/R indicators to identify red flags, and know when it's time to dig deeper to correct underlying problems and get the money collected. There are a few benchmarks that should be looked at each month. When the practice doesn't fall within the norm, start digging. The benchmarks vary by specialty, but these general benchmarks provide a good starting point for evaluating A/R performance:

- Total accounts receivable less than two times monthly charges;
- Less than 20% of total receivables aged at 120 days or older; and
- Collection ratio of 95% of adjusted charges (adjusted charges are calculated by subtracting contractual adjustments from the monthly charges).

Third Party-Reimbursement Analysis

Develop a procedure for spot-checking EOBs to be sure the insurance plan paid the claim correctly and the billing department properly audited the claim and made the appropriate contractual adjustment. Errors in this process can be very costly to the practice. I've seen as much as $200,000 inappropriately adjusted off accounts because employees assumed the insurance company paid the right fee for each service. There was one situation where the billing department was reading Medicare EOBs incorrectly and wrote off the 20% patient responsibility, amounting to $83,000 in one year. Give the responsibility for auditing claims the attention it deserves! Properly train employees and monitor outcomes.

The EOB also reports denied payment for a service. Be sure the staff appeals these claims when warranted. If the denial is a result of coding errors, it's important to inform the providers and show them how to properly code the service in the future.

Where's the Money?

If the A/R more than 120-days old rises above the norm, run a report on aging by payer class. This will identify a potential troublesome payer. The administrator can then take quick action to recover the money. The out-of-norm aging could be the result of claims kicked back to the practice with errors, or claims might be stockpiled on the desk of someone at the insurance plan. It might even be an indication that the insurance plan has financial trouble causing it to stall payments. The faster you take action, the better the chance of collecting the revenue.

There might also be large patient balances driving up the aged receivables. Perhaps the practice is keeping "dead wood" on the books. If accounts are uncollectible, the sooner they are turned over to a collection agency, the better the chance of recovery. If the practice has not received payment after four months of sending a patient statements, send the account out to a collection agency and write it off the books. However, when this happens, it's time to tighten the financial policies on patient responsibility and improve collection procedures:

1. Telephone patients for payment when a second statement does not result in payment. Phone calls are far more effective than patient statements, which are silent.
2. Critique the patient statements. Are they are easy to understand, and do they clearly show the patient what is owed?
3. Review the current dunning messages. Perhaps the messages need to be progressively stronger to get the patient's attention.
4. Consider a pre-collection letter-writing service, such as Transworld Systems, to boost patient collections.

Patient collections are one of the most challenging responsibilities in the office, and sometimes the staff needs a little motivation. Setting collection target goals and offering incentives to collectors may improve the practice's performance in this area. With employers passing more of the financial responsibility for medical care to patients, physicians and administrators need to pay close attention to how well this aspect of collections is managed.

WHOSE PRACTICE IS IT, ANYWAY?

It begins with contracting and ends with collections, but every decision and step along the way influences the ability to get paid for what you do. Physicians need to assume responsibility for these decisions and take back the control of practice finances. Sometimes that means learning to say NO. When you aren't satisfied, do something about it! If it's the payer, go back to the drawing board to negotiate and agree on revised contract terms. If the situation warrants it, fire the payer.

If it's a staff training or performance issue, address it. Give staff members the tools to do their job and hold them accountable. It's your practice!

THE EMBEZZLER

Poor financial record keeping and blind trust are invitations for embezzlement. Most physicians and administrators know someone that has been a victim of a financial scam to embezzle from a medical practice. Embezzlement is an orchestrated illegal plan to part you from your money without your knowledge.

The clever embezzler lures his victim into a false sense of security and complacency, gains trust and then tests the waters. If he gets away with it (and they usually do), he becomes confident and continues the scam.

Don't be the culprit of an embezzlement scheme that has your practice financing someone else's vacation home or kids' college education. Do what it takes to protect the practice revenue, and get the practice in "protective financial order."

Take Financial Notice

I have observed a number of practices where finances are handled casually: cash loosely kept in drawers and not reconciled to practice records before it hits the bank deposit, bank statements only looked at by the office bookkeeper, the computer system with a poor audit trail, no policy or oversight for adjustments on patient accounts and payroll records not scrutinized. On the physicians' part, this casual response to handle finances may be neglect or perhaps "too much" trust. Either way, it provides an opportunity for embezzlement and may, in fact, encourage it.

Embezzlement can occur at many locations throughout the office. It can be at the front desk, the insurance department, payroll or the accounts payable. But it almost always starts small! It can begin by borrowing $10 from the cash drawer for lunch, but if it doesn't get repaid and goes unnoticed the waters have been tested. The thief now has "permission" to take the next step.

Separation of Duties

Efficiency of a medical office depends on streamlining procedures and avoiding duplication of tasks. At the same time, multiple people need to be involved in finances, creating a separation of duties. Don't have one person audit the cash drawer, post the charge and payment and take the money to the bank. It's important that the person who prepares the checks is not the same one that reconciles the bank statement.

Create essential financial-role diversity by requiring anyone handling finances to rotate out of the position for a period of at least two consecutive weeks each year. If someone has something to hide, she sure doesn't want someone else doing her job for two weeks. This discourages the thief, but it's not foolproof. Clever employees can sometimes find ways to outsmart the system or clean up their act during the weeks proceeding their time off. They are deceptive and will do what it takes to avoid discovery.

Beyond having multiple people involved in financial transactions, it is equally important to have processes that ensure clear and appropriate documentation to support all financial transactions—money in and money out. This documentation serves as the audit trail. It allows the practice to spot-check, ensuring the financial processes are being adhered to. This is one case where duplicate efforts are a powerful financial tool.

Looking over someone's shoulder occasionally helps keep him honest. In a small practice, the doctor or an independent source such as the accountant or consultant can be the point person for accountability. A larger practice may use an independent source or have an audit committee composed of employees from various departments. Administrators and physicians need to make periodic financial reviews and audits a priority. Here are 12 simple rules you can put in place that will go a long way toward protecting practice finances:

1. Use an automated check-writing system that prints checks and leaves no room for alteration.

2. Have a bank lockbox for receiving all mail in payments on patient accounts.
3. Audit the cash drawer daily.
4. Never borrow from the cash box (or others will).
5. Eliminate signature stamps with the same names as the signers on bank accounts.
6. Have bank statements come to the home of one of the physicians and have someone that neither writes the checks nor makes the bank deposits complete the reconciliation.
7. If a nonowner of the practice is permitted to be a signer on the bank account, limit the dollar amount approved.
8. Audit payroll records semi-annually for unauthorized raises, bonuses or overtime pay.
9. Conduct past reference checks on all employees before you hire them.
10. Purchase insurance bonds on employees that handle money, but keep in mind this does not cover neglect.
11. Spot-check financial transactions and records, including adjustments on patient accounts.
12. Listen to your instincts. If you become suspicious, start digging.

Establish strong financial safeguards for the practice and adhere to them. It's a matter of sound business principles and a prudent way to conduct business. Existing employees will appreciate a solid foundation and a clear understanding of how things need to be done. New hires will recognize the practice's respect for finances and know what is expected of them. They will understand this practice "minds the store."

Communicate Consequences

As a final note, during each employee's orientation discuss the financial principles of the practice and let the new employee know you will not tolerate deceit, fraud or theft. Too many practices leave financial matters unspoken, and too many physicians that have been the victim of embezzlement fail to prosecute. Let your staff know you would!

The Secrets

1. Getting paid for what you do begins with contracting issues.
2. Scrutinize contracts and make your own contracting decisions.
3. Conduct internal chart audits.

4. Look at E&M coding patterns.
5. Monitor charge entry, claims submission and payment-timing trends.
6. Audit contract payments and adjustments for accuracy.
7. Know when to terminate a payer.
8. Establish standards for managing revenue processes.
9. Patients will assume more financial responsibility for medical care in the future.
10. Tighten procedures and controls for patient financial responsibility, including OTC payments.
11. Take charge of practice finances, and hold people accountable.
12. Take proactive steps to avoid embezzlement.

FORMS ADDED TO YOUR TOOLBOX:

☞ *Payer Performance Table* (p. 164)

Great Employees—
The Simple Truth!

What hasn't been said or written about the difficulty in managing human resources (HR)? When HR troubles rise to the top of management's concerns, they can encompass a menagerie of problems: turnover, overtime, poor attendance, poor attitude, low productivity, lack of respect—you name it! It's all about people; what they bring to and how they feel about the workplace. When it's not working, there are major headaches.

KEY FACT: *When employees believe they work "with" the practice, rather than "for" the practice, they become an intricate part of the practice's success.*

Everyone is searching for the best employees. You look for ways to improve your recruitment efforts through better screening tools and testing instruments. You hone your interview skills and improve your analysis of applicants. In the end, it's a gamble and just a matter of improving your odds.

While it's not easy to find peak-performing employees, the poor performers surely will make their presence felt. You know the old 80/20 rule: you spend 80% of your time dealing with 20% of the people. Most often, unfortunately, the problem employees get the attention, and sometimes this investment of management's time doesn't pay off. The top-performing, dedicated employees are worthy of our time—the ones we'd like to clone. The great ones! So what are the secrets to making a great employee? How do you turn ordinary people into great employees? I'm about to tell you the simple truths I've learned.

The best employees are not molded by the technical skills managers apply. The best employees are not created by the things taught in the HR classes you took in college. The best employees are not created through rigorous academic analysis or through textbook applications. These tools are useful in helping understand employees and discovering ways to approach HR management, but they are not at the core of what makes great employees.

LOOK AT ROBIN

Take Robin, for example. Robin worked with Las Posas Family Practice, a five-physician medical group, for more than 10 years. Notice I said she worked *with* the practice and not *for* the practice. There's a big difference. Working for a practice is doing a job. Working with the practice is being an intricate part of the business—taking responsibility for what you do and pride in what you accomplish for the practice. That's Robin!

Providing and Taking Opportunity

Robin started working with Las Posas Family Practice when she was a college student. She worked her way up from file clerk to managing the billing department. Robin was thirsty for knowledge, taking every opportunity to learn more and expand her skills. The physicians and manager of this practice, by the same token, recognized Robin's potential and opened up the doors of opportunity. Everyone benefited. Robin gained confidence and knew she was valued. Management could depend on Robin whenever she was called on to learn a new task or assume more responsibility. She became the model employee.

Character Counts

We all know character plays a vital role in the value of an employee and his or her contribution in the workplace. Robin is a perfect example. She is dedicated, honest, dependable, flexible, open-minded and sincere. These are character traits that start you on the road to building a great employee. Let's look at what these character traits do for business performance and professional growth:

- Dedicated employees are loyal and represent the practice in a favorable manner. They take their job seriously, and it shows in their performance.
- Honest employees have better attendance—management and coworkers can depend on them. They are considerate and respectful of superiors and peers.
- Employees that are flexible and open-minded become excellent team players. They adapt to a changing environment and pitch in when other

workers need a hand. They learn how to solve problems and how to help other people solve problems. They are quick to find a more-efficient way to get something done and are sincere in their interactions with patients, staff and management.

These character traits are the core of what becomes a model employee. While you should try to hire those with desirable character traits, management's ideals, attitudes and actions largely determine if the employee excels.

People with questionable character traits simply aren't going to become great employees. Good managers can strengthen the character of staff if there's a solid foundation, but building character is not your job. If you focus on building character into employees, you will be falling victim to the old 80/20 rule. You will spend endless hours trying to shape employees who, in the end, are not going to make the same investment in the practice—and don't discount the possible negative impact on the rest of the staff. Don't alienate staff or waste your time. Naturally, problem employees often require some meaningful attention, but spend the bulk of your time where you'll reap a better return on your investment.

Believe in Your Heart

Believing in your heart isn't meant to sound soft or sentimental. Physicians and administrators at the helm of a great practice are instrumental in creating a culture that tells employees they are valued. To create great employees, you must believe in your heart that they can excel and be great at what they do.

Take Robin. When I asked her what was great about her job at Las Posas Family Practice, she brightened up and couldn't stop talking. She told how she was just a college student when she came to work at Las Posas and how they gave her a chance. They worked around her hours, and when they moved her from file clerk to receptionist they believed she could do the job at a time when she wasn't quite so sure. They encouraged her, giving her more responsibility and more support. She said the doctors had a "can do" attitude, always believing in and encouraging staff.

Robin told me how her confidence grew and that everything she achieved at Las Posas was because the physicians believed in her. She told me how respectful and caring they were to the patients and staff. They gave her extra time off and were truly sympathetic when a family emergency occurred.

She talked about the terrific Christmas parties, always hosted by one of the physicians in his home. The physicians at Las Posas Family Practice created a wonderful culture, and demonstrated how much they valued Robin— they believed in her ability in their hearts.

Take Susan—the "Perfect Receptionist" in Chapter 1. She certainly understands the value she brings to the practice. She knows she has an important job and that management will provide her with whatever support she needs. Susan has confidence, feels appreciated and loves her job. Employees only feel this way when management is sincere and recognizes their value and that their contribution is part of management's own success! Management leads the way in making the difference between mediocre and great employees.

GET OFF TO A GOOD START

Wouldn't it be wonderful if at the end of the first day on the new job every employee went home feeling like they had the perfect job and a great employer? With a little effort and a big commitment, you have the ability to make new employees feel that working for you is one of the best decisions they ever made.

It starts with first impressions and what you do to develop a positive experience for the new employee. Ask Laura Sachs Hills, the author of *How to Recruit, Motivate, and Manage a Winning Staff*, a fantastic how-to book (Greenbranch Publishing, 2004). Laura says, "With a little planning and effort, the new employee can have a positive start and quickly become a motivated and productive member of your team." Laura is right, it's up to you. You hold all the cards in your hand.

Here are a few of her ideas on how to integrate new employees into the practice and give them the sense that they belong from day one:

1. Plan ahead and provide the essentials. This includes clearing the employee's workspace—desk, cabinets, bulletin board, telephone, etc. Make sure the space is clean and stocked with fresh supplies and properly functioning equipment. Remove personal items left by former employees.

2. Engrave a nametag for the new employee and a desk or office-door sign with his or her name and title, if appropriate.

3. Introduce the new employee to each member of your staff. Explain each person's responsibilities and job duties. If the employee will be

supervised by your office or clinical manager, or another person, introduce him or her.

4. Outline what the new employee is to do that day and throughout the orientation period. Prepare a checklist of all the tasks to be learned and who in your office will do the training. Choose trainers who have mastered the task and who are willing and capable teachers.

5. Give the new employee a guided tour of the office. Point out the staff restroom, coat/storage closet, and break room.

6. Capture your new employee's debut on film. The day will come when you introduce a new employee to his or her first patient. This is a big moment for many new employees and particularly for new associates fresh out of school. Don't let this moment come and go unnoticed.

7. Assign one staff member the task of being the new employee's "buddy." He or she will serve as your new employee's mentor and troubleshooter.

Here are a few of my own ideas to add to the list:

1. Prepare a brief biographical sketch of the employee to include on a welcome flyer with his photo. Include a little about his professional background, but personal information is even more important. State how long he has lived in the community, tell a little about his family, favorite hobbies, food and perhaps his favorite vacation, sports team or whatever. Pass a copy out to each employee before the new employee starts.

2. Introduce the new employee to patients by enlarging the biographical flyer onto poster board that is placed on an easel in the reception room. Add a header "Meet our latest addition!"

3. Provide the employee with a fact sheet about the practice. This should include the names of each physician and when he or she first entered the practice, a list of employees including their titles and phone extension, the practice's philosophy and mission statement and answers to the 10 most common questions patients ask.

4. Have a staff luncheon in honor of the employee during the first week of employment.

5. Have the new employee's immediate supervisor meet with him at the end of each day during the first week or so. Answer questions, and give the new employee encouragement or support as needed.

6. Take a photo of the new employee on the first day of work and have it enlarged for the staff bulletin board. Take some additional "at work"

photos (during the first month) that can be added to the practice's photo album/scrapbook. Circulate the scrapbook at the next staff meeting.

Why is all this effort dedicated to a new employee so important? In the words of Laura Sachs Hills, "What you do from the moment your new employee steps into your office can determine whether she becomes an asset or a liability. Just a little bit of extra attention to this critical time can reduce your turnover and speed the new employee's acclimation to your practice." I couldn't agree more. This up-front investment you make sends the new employee a strong message about his new workplace and how you treat and value employees.

THE VISIBLE MANAGER

Managers and physicians have awesome responsibilities. Sometimes there is just so much to do in a day, a week, a month that they are easily buried in administrative and clinical responsibilities. This can, unintentionally, leave little time dedicated to staff and staff responsibilities. Unfortunately, this often results in staff feeling that the doctors and managers are unapproachable. It can even cause employees to feel like their problems are too small to bring to their supervisor's attention. When this occurs, a wall forms between management and staff that can be troublesome.

If staff members do not feel comfortable going to managers, they will begin making decisions on their own that they are neither authorized nor equipped to make. They may muddle their way through a problem hoping to solve it without their supervisor ever knowing about it. This breakdown in communication sometimes compromises the end result of the very problem they are trying to fix. Staff members may feel they don't have the support needed to do the job right. Be sensitive to the nonverbal messages your actions (or failure to act) send to employees.

No matter how busy you are, it's important to walk the floor and circulate. When you mingle with employees while they are working, you not only connect with them, you also learn about their work processes as well as problems and areas of the practice that are changing. For example, you may see patient bottlenecks at the exit station that didn't used to exist. What has caused this change? Is it because Jennifer can't keep up since she has taken on more tasks? Has the computer slowed down? Are there more patients? You may see other situations that are worthy of your attention— like a mound of filing stacked up in the medical records department.

Talk to the employees: see what they are doing and what they need. Find out what difficulties they confront and give encouragement and praise. Your visibility demonstrates the commitment to your staff members and interest in the challenges they face each day.

How approachable are you?

- Are you the physician that walks in the back door and either heads for your office or immediately starts seeing patients without acknowledging the staff, or are you the physician that greets everyone and pays special attention to new employees?
- Are you the physician that skips out of staff meetings because you have something more important to do, or are you the one that knows the meeting is an opportunity to connect with staff members and find out what's on their minds?
- Are you the administrator that is squirreled away in your office going over important reports and meeting with decision makers, or are you the administrator that carves out time each day to survey the office to see how staff is doing and give your support?
- Are you the practice executive that meets with staff members only when you need to reprimand them, or are you the special manager that calls someone into your office for a little encouragement or praise?
- Are you the manager that puts off performance reviews because they are a nuisance and take up so much time, or do you schedule these reviews when they are due because you recognize reviews are an opportunity to connect with employees, offer constructive criticism, acknowledge achievements and guide good employees on the road to becoming great employees?

If you want the best from your employees, create a united front and show your appreciation—be there, be visible.

OPEN COMMUNICATION

Open communication means *exchanging* information—speaking and listening. Open communication allows people to speak freely and honestly to understand another's point of view. That's a powerful tool. Sometimes spontaneous communication is best. In other words, if someone has something on her mind and is given the opportunity to talk about it, each of you will understand the other and will not be left to form erroneous opinions. When managers are available and encourage employees to come to them with concerns, they can detect problems, nip them in the bud and encourage further communication and problem solving.

How do you encourage open communication? Begin with setting a communication policy whereby employees go first to their supervisor with problems, rather than bypassing this level and going to the practice administrator or a physician to get questions answered and problems solved. Managers and physicians should reinforce this policy. This policy should hold for both business and clinical staff. There is sometimes a tendency for clinical staff members to go directly to the doctors rather than their supervisors. Doctors need to discourage such actions.

Next, establish times when you are available to employees. Since the first few hours of the morning yield the highest production if uninterrupted, allow employees to come into your office between 11:00 AM and 12:30 PM each day and again during the last hour of the day. With this type of schedule, you are available to discuss major issues; but employees won't be able to immediately come to you with minor problems, so they may be more inclined to resolve these types of problems on their own.

Take Time to Connect

If you are in charge of an office large enough to have managers for each department, you may want to have management huddles for a half-hour each day or weekly brown-bag lunch meetings. In a smaller office, a morning huddle with the entire staff can be an excellent way to start the day. Such investments of time help everyone plan their day and head off minor problems before they erupt into something bigger.

Regular staff meetings allow for interoffice and interdepartmental communication and exchange of ideas. They also are an opportunity to discuss policy and procedural changes and announce activities that are in the practice pipeline. When information is relayed at a staff meeting, everyone hears the same thing at the same time, eliminating room for miscommunication. Staff meetings also encourage open dialogue, allowing for clarification and a chance for staff members to state their opinions or offer suggestions. This is a far-more-effective method to inform staff than relaying information through appointed messengers. The "grapevine" approach results in misinterpretation or failure to fully communicate the same information to everyone.

Rules of meetings include planning, creating and following a prepared agenda, staying on time, encouraging the entire staff to participate and documenting action items with a target date and who is assigned to handle the task. Reinforce the importance of meetings by not canceling them unless absolutely necessary and not reacting to trivial office circumstances by calling unnecessary meetings that disrupt workflow and interfere with maintaining a calm and productive environment.

Memos are an important way to communicate time-sensitive information between meetings. Memos can be distributed by posting on a bulletin board, hand-delivering hard copies or sending electronically through interoffice email. Whatever form you choose, it's important that all employees get their copy in the same time frame. If one person is left out of the loop, the communication breakdown can be damaging. A word of caution on the use of memos: Do not use memos to avoid open dialogue as this can cause staff resentment. Memos cannot replace one-on-one communication or meetings with open discussion.

One-on-one meetings should be considered unique events. If they happen too often, they lose their importance. If they are scheduled too infrequently, you are not connecting with individuals that you value. One-on-one meetings are best when regarded as special—the annual performance review, the announcement of a promotion and the occasional time you simply call someone in to tell him he is doing a good job and to keep up the good work. Hopefully, this communication inspires people to give their best, resulting in less need to call people in because their performance is deteriorating. However, such meetings are occasionally necessary, and it's vitally important that any employee criticism be done in private. Remember the saying, "praise in public, criticize in private." Public criticism is devastating to morale and shows a lack of respect for staff.

MAKE EVERYONE A WINNER

Develop a culture that inspires staff members to do their best. This ongoing process starts at the top. There are a number of ways a practice develops a culture that empowers staff to be productive and enrich the practice. The skillful manager develops a relationship with each individual member of the staff to better understand what each person needs and wants from the job. Beyond the obvious advantage of feeling a sense of belonging, what motivates Melissa may not be what motivates Tom. Get to know your employees and how you can contribute to their success. Think outside the box and be creative.

Giving to Employees

There are many ways the practice can give more to its employees, and it's not always a financial investment. This is why it is essential to understand what motivates your employees and to recognize their broader needs. There is a multitude of ways to invest in staff members and make them feel important. With a little thought and creativity you can give them what they need and will appreciate—something that is mutually beneficial.

For example, young mothers that work might prefer working part-time around their children's school hours to avoid paying for childcare that would take a big chunk of their pay check. Some employees like flexible schedules or job sharing. These are things you can offer that don't add to your staffing costs, but go a long way in recognizing the needs of employees and gaining their loyalty. And when it comes to job sharing and part-time workers, these are the employees you can count on when someone is on vacation or out sick. These employees are the ones that provide needed support when workloads fluctuate or the practice experiences temporary demands such as a computer conversion, opening a satellite office or bringing a new doctor on board.

On the other hand, you may have several employees that are taking college courses at night. Giving a $100 book stipend each semester is a wonderful way to honor your employees' dedication to furthering their education. Your investment can provide job enrichment and rewards for employees. Take the medical assistant that wants to return to school and obtain her RN. There are many ways to support her effort. Perhaps you might offer to move her to part time so she can attend classes two afternoons each week, or you might commit to pay a percentage of the costs for her schooling and/or giving her a one-time bonus if she stays on with the practice for a stated length of time after she becomes registered.

Perhaps you have an employee that has his limited x-ray license but aspires to be a magnetic resonance imaging (MRI) technician. This might be the opportunity to explore his desires and match them to your needs. Maybe the number of MRIs the practice is referring out justifies bringing this service in house. If so, establishing a time line that brings MRI aboard at the same time this employee is finishing his training would be mutually beneficial.

Send employees (at your expense and on the practice's clock) to workshops and seminars that enhance their on-the-job skills and keep them current in their field. Don't limit training to clinical courses or coding. All employees need to hone their skills from time to time. A day out of the office with peers from other practices can be energizing, and employees will return with tips to help them on the job. Job enrichment is an important element in obtaining peak performance. You can emphasize employee value while boosting their confidence by having employees share what they learned at the next staff meeting.

Be a Joiner

Ask your staff to participate in professional organizations, and have the practice pay the fees. For management staff, there is the Professional Association of Health Care Office Management (PAHCOM; www.pahcom.com) and the Medical Group Management Association (MGMA; www.mgma.com), both of which have certification programs that help their members expand their knowledge base and obtain recognition for it. What they learn through certification programs, conferences or workshops will apply to their job.

There are also specialty organizations for other positions in the practice. You may want your head nurse to belong to the National Association of Healthcare Quality (www.nahq.org), and your coder can become certified with the American Academy of Professional Coders (www.aapc.com). This all makes for stronger staff and a stronger practice. Employees are one of your greatest assets—let your actions show how you value them!

Coaching

Coaching is a matter of creating a climate where everyone wins. The attention you give to employees and the attention every member of the team gives to each other is the yardstick for measuring your success as captain of the team. It's unrealistic to expect that each employee will become great, but if all members of the team are performing at close to their potential, you have achieved the goal of the coach. And if we continually raise the bar on our expectations for group performance, individual performance also rises.

Management must fulfill its promises to staff and remain steadfast in defining and communicating goals. Everyone must be held to the same high standard. If Krista at the front desk is expected to be on time every morning, Jason in billing should be expected to be on time as well. Your policies and actions must reflect a commitment to consistency and fairness.

Here's a simple way to check your consistency with your team members. Create a list composed of three columns labeled "Great," "Good" and "Poor." Classify each employee under one of these columns. Now pull the HR files and compare each person's last performance review with the category you gave him or her. If it doesn't match, inconsistencies exist in the standards you maintain for staff. To improve the performance of average and low performers, you must expect them to meet predetermined standards evenly applied across the board. They need to know you have expectations you will hold them to. Meanwhile, don't forget that constructive criticism and encouragement are essential to improving the outcome.

Your top-performing employees need attention and recognition as well. The visible manager understands that everyone needs appreciation, support and reassurance from time to time.

About the Money

People work for reasons other than money, although money certainly plays an important role. It has been my experience that employees with a job they enjoy and a practice they feel truly involved in don't leave for an extra dollar an hour. That being said, pay people what they are worth!

The amount of education and experience and job responsibilities should dictate the variance between one position and another in weighting the pay rate. For example, there would be a natural differential between the receptionist and the billing supervisor's job requirements and pay rate. Develop job descriptions that define the criteria for each position, and weight the base of pay accordingly. Once you have established a weight, the traditional pay rates for your geographic area will dictate the supply-and-demand aspects that influence pay scales.

Gather information from local and national sources regarding pay rates to use as a baseline. Check with your chamber of commerce, employment agencies, the local medical society and other medical practices to find out what the "going rate" is. Statistical information on salaries specifically for health care professionals is also available through MGMA, PAHCOM and the Health Care Group (www.healthcaregroup.com).

Setting wages is not the place to skimp. Employers that pay in the top 20% of the area's medical practices generally do so because their employees are worth it. Pay staff fairly, but don't pay more than you should. I've seen practices where two employees sit side-by-side, with the same skills, doing the same job, and the new employee is making 30% more than the other. This is not reasonable or fair. Problems occur when you don't establish salary ranges for each position and stick with them. It happens when we are interviewing and make an emotional decision to hire someone asking for a pay rate that doesn't fit with the existing job requirements and responsibilities. The candidate may have been paid more in her last position because she assumed more responsibilities or lived in an area where salaries are traditionally higher. Don't be enticed by demands for a higher salary. Take this opportunity to inform the applicant by reviewing the job description, discussing how you arrived at the salary range for the position and why you cannot go beyond the structured range to hire her.

Letting Go

All good things come to end, and so it will be with your great employees. If you are lucky enough to have them on board for five to eight years, count your blessings. Eventually it will be time for them to move on. They have served you well, but the time has arrived when they seek new challenges. When they leave, both of you are better off than you were before the employee was hired. Robin is a perfect example. She did a great job running the billing department of Las Posas Family Practice, but she moved on to a new opportunity and continued to grow. I know this, because Robin came to work with me. I owe much of my own success to Robin—and I believe this in my heart. When it was time for us to part, I felt a great sadness, but I knew she would do well wherever she went. I remain close to Robin and am grateful for all she has done for me. I expect great things from her and eagerly follow her ultimate success.

NO-TOLERANCE POLICY

Turn the old 80/20 rule on its heels. You don't have 80% of your time to dedicate to the poor performer, so don't do it. You know the poor employee—the one who doesn't want to do his fair share of the work, is irresponsible or has a bad attitude. It's easy to detect. Sometimes we avoid dealing with the poor performer in hopes that things will get better. Face the music—in most cases improvement is not likely.

When performance is slipping, give the person an opportunity to improve, but hold to your high standards. Don't waiver. Even though the employee may have great skills for the job, if he isn't committed or simply doesn't fit in your practice it's best to deal with it sooner rather than later. Besides, there's the "poisoned well" syndrome. It doesn't take long for the employee with a bad attitude to get things brewing among the staff. Morale will quickly deteriorate unless you develop a no-tolerance policy.

Performance issues require a tiered approach to resolution. You know the script. First is the verbal warning or counseling session, followed by a formal write-up and disciplinary action and finally resolution—satisfactory performance or termination. I am surprised by how many times some practices stall in the second tier. The employees are warned, but the situation is never resolved. Sometimes these practices give repeated warnings, but fail to terminate—in effect giving employees permission to continue their offending actions. It is unfair to those employees that do their job, and it compromises the practice's overall performance.

When employees are given a written warning, the expected result must be defined objectively with a specific time frame. If this goal is not met, management has the responsibility to terminate the employees.

When it becomes necessary to discharge an employee, do it with dignity. Make it brief, and give the specific reasons, but also tell him about his good points. Suggest the type of position he might pursue that more suitably matches his skills and personality traits.

YOUR #1 CUSTOMER

If you remember that employees are your first customers, you can't go wrong. Their needs and desires vary with time, as their personal lives evolve and the work environment changes. To keep tabs on whether you are on target with meeting their needs, periodically conduct an anonymous staff survey that rates management —preferably conducted by someone outside the practice, such as the accountant or practice management consultant.

Also conduct exit interviews with each staff member that resigns. Don't do this on her last day, but perhaps a week before she departs. Use this opportunity for her to critique management and provide constructive suggestions. Departing employees have a tendency to say everything is fine, so ask open-ended questions that call for more than a yes-or-no answer such as, "Sherri, you have been in our medical records department for three years. What changes have occurred during that time and how have they impacted your job?" "What could we have done to make your job easier?" "What task did you like least about your job (and why)?"

The survey and interview results can guide your efforts to keep employees motivated and productive. Managing HR is an ongoing and changing process, as you deal with different generations of staff with different expectations. Polling staff from time to time helps you understand these differences and respond accordingly.

Being an effective leader requires a combination of skill, art, instinct and respect. People achieve their best when you expect a lot from them, as long as you give a lot back and are consistently honest and fair. In essence, the simple truths all add up to treating people right!

The Secrets

1. Make employees feel valuable.
2. Provide opportunity for growth, and staff will have a vested interest in the practice.
3. Top employees start with strong character traits.
4. Express confidence in staff, and they will become confident.
5. Invest in the right employees.
6. Loyalty comes from "believing" in employees.
7. Recognize and praise individual talents.
8. Be approachable and visible every day.
9. Develop a no-tolerance policy for poor performance.

FORMS ADDED TO YOUR TOOLBOX:

∽ *Sample Bio Sketch* (p. 165)

∽ *Meeting Action Matrix* (p. 166)

∽ *Staff Survey: How Does Management Rate?* (p. 167)

∽ *Management Skills Audit* (p. 169)

CHAPTER 10

The Money Crunch

"We have a cash flow crisis and don't know how to fix it!" These were the words of Marci Bradford, M.D., the senior doctor of Evergreen Women's Center when she called my office. Despite a high demand for its services, the practice was struggling with finances, and the physicians were in a panic. The practice was financed to the max and not prepared to handle further financial obligations.

KEY FACT: *Planning for the future and monitoring progress are critical components to successful growth and financial management.*

Evergreen's financial woes were felt throughout the organization, creating quite a stir. No one was monitoring the income and expense trends, and there was never enough money to pay the bills. Through the grapevine, staff members heard about the money problems, and they were feeling uneasy. After a couple of payroll checks bounced, some of the staff began to bail. The stability and future of the practice were in question.

THEY GREW TOO FAST

I soon learned that Evergreen Women's Center was a victim of its own success. The center was started by Dr. Bradford three years prior and appeared to be an immediate success, adding two more physicians within the first year. By the end of the second year, Evergreen hired two nurse practitioners.

Dr. Bradford was planning to offer a partnership to the other physicians, but had to get the finances in order first. With the current state of affairs, this wasn't possible, and physician confidence in the practice was waning. This was a major concern for Dr. Bradford.

Evergreen Women's Center couldn't get a handle on its growth or practice finances. It took money to expand a practice and meet patient demand, but seeing more patients wasn't providing the revenue required to meet financial obligations. Dr. Bradford recently secured a lease on a second office, but Evergreen's current financial situation prevented it from equipping and opening the office. The practice was about to recruit a fourth physician when Dr. Bradford put on the brakes and called me.

In addition to the typical operating expenses, there were financial obligations for capital investment. More capital expenditures were on the horizon for the new office, and Evergreen was about to borrow more money just to keep it afloat. Evergreen needed a financial-recovery plan and needed it fast.

CHECKING OUT THE NUMBERS

In order to give Evergreen the help it sought, it was critical for me to get a clear understanding of the financial picture and what interventions would be required to get Evergreen on solid ground. I needed to see how revenue was flowing in and out of the business and examine key financial indicators. Standard financial reporting processes were not in place, so data needed to be collected from various sources and pulled together. This in itself turned out to be quite a challenge.

When I asked Dr. Bradford what financial reports she looked at each month, she expressed frustration. The practice management system generated many reports, but no one was looking at them or providing Dr. Bradford with sound financial information about the practice.

Cheryl Alexander, the practice administrator, was in charge of finances, but told Dr. Bradford she didn't have time to look at the monthly reports, yet alone analyze them. Cheryl simply knew that the amount of money collected each month was not enough to cover Evergreen's expenses. She cared deeply about the practice and was losing sleep over the state of financial affairs.

Annual financial statistics on group OB-GYN practices compiled by the Society of Medical-Dental Management Consultants/National Association of Healthcare Consultants (SMD/NAHC) and Medical Group Management Association (MGMA) were used to conduct a comparative financial analysis of Evergreen Women's Center.

The Revenue Cycle

First I needed to look at the charges, receipts, adjustments and accounts receivable (A/R) for the practice to find out if Evergreen was collecting

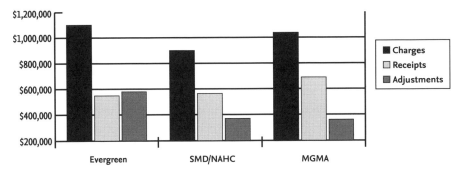

FIGURE 1. Evergreen Women's Center productivity performance comparison per full time equivalent (FTE) MD. MGMA = Medical Group Management Association; SMD/NAHC = Society of Medical-Dental Management Consultants/National Association of Healthcare Consultants.

what should be expected, based on other OB-GYN group practices across the nation. These comparisons would help determine if revenue-recovery strategies could be implemented to pump up cash flow.

The first red flag was obvious: this practice's charges and adjustments were higher than its peers, but its receipts were dismal. The practice was collecting only 48% of its charges, as opposed to a 60% collection rate reported by SMD/NAHC and a 66% collection rate by MGMA. If Evergreen's collection rate was 66%, it would have earned nearly $200,000 (per physician) in additional income during the previous year. This would have provided considerable relief to the present financial situation. Evergreen Women's Center's adjustments (contract disallowances) were 52% of charges compared with an average of 40% reported by SMD/NAHC and just under 34% for MGMA (Figure 1). This is usually an indicator of inappropriate adjustments, poor-performing contracts or an unusually high fee schedule.

I soon discovered that Evergreen's billing department was struggling. The data entry, billing and collection staff members were inundated because of the rapid growth. Systems were not in place to handle the growth and volume. Work was coming to them faster then they could handle it. Many of the claims were submitted as hard copies rather than using a clearinghouse to submit claims electronically. Claims submission was delayed by at least 30 days, and, according to a frustrated staff, there was no time to do follow-up on claims. Many claims were being rejected because the patient demographics were incomplete or inaccurate. This contributed to

TABLE 1. Accounts Receivable Details for Evergreen vs. Industry Averages

Description	Evergreen	SMD/NAHC	MGMA
Total $ of A/R	191,894	122,295	125,325
A/R % aged >90 Days	34	Unknown	15
Days in A/R	63	48	45

A/R = accounts receivable; MGMA = Medical Group Management Association; SMD/NAHC = Society of Medical-Dental Management Consultants/National Association of Healthcare Consultants.

above-average days in A/R and a total A/R of $191,894 per full time physician, more than 50% above the average OB-GYN practice (Table 1). Evergreen's money was on the books instead of in the bank.

On the back end, when payments came in there was a rush to get the money deposited and not enough time was dedicated to analyzing claims to be sure they were adjudicated properly. There were instances where the billing staff was inadvertently adjusting off balances inappropriately.

Expense Control

OB-GYN group practice operating expenses averaged nearly 57% of receipts as reported by SMD/NAHC and close to 53% reported by MGMA. Unfortunately, Evergreen Women's Center's expenses were far higher—an alarming 78% of gross income. With an excessive practice overhead cost, only 22% of the gross income was left to pay the physicians and pay down the debt. It wasn't enough! Expenses were killing this practice.

The largest contributor to these out-of-bounds operating expenses were: staff, staff benefits and rent. Staffing and staff benefits combined contributed to 46% of the practice's overhead and needed immediate attention (Table 2).

TABLE 2. Evergreen's Expenses vs. Industry Average

Description (% of receipts)	Evergreen	SMD/NAHC	MGMA
Staffing	39	21	27
Staff benefits	7	4	5
Rent	9	5	7
Combined total	55	30	39

MGMA = Medical Group Management Association; SMD/NAHC = Society of Medical-Dental Management Consultants/National Association of Healthcare Consultants.

Malpractice insurance was another contributor to high overhead costs, as rates had continually escalated since the practice opened. Because malpractice premium rates are geographically sensitive, this could not be realistically compared to national data. Certainly, options could be explored with the objective of reducing this cost in the future.

THE INFRASTRUCTURE

The administrative review revealed an administrative vacuum, a large contributor to Evergreen's problems. Dr. Bradford was a respected leader and was, without question, the driving force behind the practice's growth and community presence. However, the infrastructure was weak. Throughout the hierarchy, there were no clear expectations or accountability. There was little delineation of duties and responsibilities, beginning with the administrator all the way down to the file clerk.

Too much was being expected of Cheryl, the administrator. Her role needed to be clearly defined and designed to utilize her talents. She had a strong financial background and was devoted to the practice. Her analytical skills made her a fine candidate to handle the practice finances but she needed direction and structure.

Cheryl preferred working with finances and was frustrated by the other responsibilities that seemed to sabotage her ability to focus on the financial picture. It was easy to see why Cheryl was unable to dedicate time to performing financial analysis. She was bombarded with day-to-day problems that she didn't have the time to deal with, and her workload was unmanageable. She was trying to handle the finances and practice administration while being pulled into crisis situations. In addition, the physicians would continually call upon her to handle minor projects. With proper planning, it was reasonable to assume that many of these projects could be delegated to other staff members.

Staffing

Staff growth was out of control and resulted in staffing levels far above the norm (Table 3) with poor definition of roles. If one department said it needed help and couldn't manage the workload, another staffer was recruited. This occurred without analyzing efficiency or work processes that would define the actual need. In other words, staff was increased based on perceived needs rather than determining actual needs. Not only was this a financial

TABLE 3. OB-GYN Group Practice Staffing Benchmark Comparatives

Organization	Staff (per FTE physician)
Evergreen	6.1
SMD/NAHC	3.6
MGMA	4.6

FTE = full-time equivalent; MGMA = Medical Group Management Association; SMD/NAHC = Society of Medical-Dental Management Consultants/National Association of Healthcare Consultants.

concern, it represented a loss of control and was a source of frustration throughout the organization.

There were no written job descriptions. Without a clear delineation of duties, there was no way to know what was expected of staff members. In addition, work measurement tools were not in place, making it difficult (if not impossible) for employees to know if they were doing a good job. This also compromised the ability to measure productivity at every level. The best performers were not being recognized, and there were no consequences for under performance.

How Decisions Were Made

Planning was inadequate, resulting in poor decision making. The practice was reacting to circumstances rather than acting on information. It seemed Dr. Bradford was always called upon to intervene when problems erupted that required a management decision. The practice resorted to continual "crisis management." This was both inefficient and costly to the practice.

The organizational chart was linear, drawing too few people into authoritative, decision-making positions. There were only three levels on the organizational chart:

- Physician/owner (Dr. Bradford);
- Administrator (Cheryl Alexander); and
- Everyone else.

This linear approach to the organization was choking Dr. Bradford and Cheryl. It contributed to the loss of control, poor decision making and inadequate management resources. Cheryl did not meet regularly with Dr. Bradford to discuss emerging issues and concerns. At the same time, Dr. Bradford did not meet with the other physicians or include them in any of management's decisions.

There were no staff meetings to keep staff connected, provide support among staff members and different departments or to communicate information about the practice. Communication was often disseminated through informal channels, such as when only one staff member was told about a change that impacted an entire department. Naturally this staff member would be left to his or her own discretion to relay information to other employees. This approach to communication was wide open to subjective interpretation and delivered throughout the organization with inconsistency. Often sensitive information told to one person in confidence ended up in the rumor mill, causing considerable distress and confusion.

THE FINAL DIAGNOSIS

Although Evergreen's problems seemed overwhelming, once the situation was thoroughly explored six major contributors to the practice's state of affairs were identified. Addressing these factors was essential to getting the practice back on course.

1. No clear direction;
2. Lack of planning;
3. Inadequate infrastructure;
4. Poor use of resources;
5. Lack of financial management; and
6. Improper decision making.

NO PAIN, NO GAIN

Immediate interventions were required and tough decisions needed to be made to help this practice survive. This required an aggressive survival plan: pumping up the revenue and cutting expenses to the core. It included a reduction in staff and some temporary pay cuts. Dr. Bradford's commitment to the practice and loyalty to staff and patients made it difficult for her to accept this reality, but it was time to put emotions aside.

Efforts focused on stopping the flow of red ink, strengthening the administrative arm of the practice and developing effective methods to monitor critical financial data. This was a challenge that required both a swift, decisive plan and the support of management and staff. Dr. Bradford was ready to listen to her advisors and do what was necessary to save the practice.

TURNAROUND STRATEGIES

The key components for a successful turnaround included:

- Responding to critical data;
- Defining expectations;
- Eliminating waste and duplication;
- Implementing and adhering to a budget;
- Planning effectively and improving decision making;
- Developing a skilled leadership team; and
- Improving communication throughout the organization.

Interim Leadership Team

It was critical to recruit an administrator with the leadership, organizational and business talents essential to oversee the practice's operations and business performance. From past experience, I knew this could easily take three to four months. In the meantime, Dr. Bradford agreed to have my consulting team provide interim leadership services. The consulting team was charged with the reorganization, leading the financial turnaround and implementing sound financial strategies.

Cheryl was reassigned to the position of staff accountant, which freed her to provide the consultants with constant status reports on practice finances. She was relieved to have someone else assume responsibility for handling the practice's administrative burdens and decision making during this critical transition.

The success of the turnaround was dependent on selecting a project coordinator to work closely with the consultants to carry out staff assignments and be our communication link. Angela Lopez, the lead biller, was a logical choice. She had previous management experience, possessed organizational and leadership skills and was respected by the staff. She was totally committed to Evergreen and was invaluable as the point person.

THE ACTION PLAN

The first response to critical data was placing an immediate freeze on hiring and capital spending, followed by an analysis of staff duties and performance to increase output. A financial-recovery plan was developed to maximize resources and expedite billing and collection activities.

The obvious approach to getting this practice on a sound financial footing was dependent on five basic objectives:

1. Maximize physician and staff productivity;
2. Improve charge capture;
3. Optimize revenue recovery;
4. Reduce expenses; and
5. Control capital outlay.

Action grids were prepared outlining responsibilities of the consultant team and the staff accountant (Figures 2 and 3). These action grids were reviewed with Dr. Bradford, the other physicians, Cheryl and Angela. It was important for each of these people to understand the goals and the commitment necessary to move the practice through difficult times. Without their support, it would be a difficult road to recovery.

In the end, everyone wanted the same things: direction, structure, stability and financial viability. The staff and physicians understood this would not be easy to achieve and would require their support. Through mutual respect, flexibility and building a solid foundation, progress continued at a reasonable pace and confidence in the practice was eventually restored.

Before the action plan was implemented, two meetings were scheduled to discuss the dire state of affairs, communicate the need for immediate recovery actions and solicit support. This required careful and deliberate planning to ensure the physicians and staff would have hope for the future of the practice and commit to the changes required to achieve viability for a practice that appeared to have a dynamic future—if only it could get its finances under control.

These meetings set the record straight and truncated the distorted grapevine approach to communication that previously relayed inaccurate information, resulting in fear and diminished confidence in management's ability to solve major problems. It was time to lay the cards on the table and tell everyone about the practice's financial situation and let them know how it would be resolved. This was particularly difficult for Dr. Bradford, as she was not accustomed to sharing information or involving staff in the practice's business affairs. It required several management meetings to agree on what information needed to be shared with the employees—in fairness to them and to obtain their support. We wanted the staff to know the situation was serious, but that a recovery plan was in place. The con-

CONSULTANT TEAM / INTERIM ADMINISTRATOR		
Action	**Deadline**	**Purpose**
Select project coordinator	Immediate	Provide coordination and support of required actions
Recruit and hire new administrator	60 days	Improve leadership and organizational function
Assign staff members to complete job description questionnaire for creating new job descriptions	3 days	Understand current workflow
Collect workload data	10 days	Evaluate staffing needs to improve efficiency
Establish and enforce collection criteria	7 days	Improve cash flow
Assign billing supervisor and establish collection criteria/goals	Immediate	Empower and mentor billing staff
Establish charge reporting and claims submission time limits	7 days	Tighten revenue cycle, improve cash flow
Implement improved coding application and charge reporting	10 days	Improve financial performance
Conduct payer analysis and renegotiate with or terminate poor-performing contracts where contract terms permit	90 days	Improve financial performance
Develop job descriptions and performance standards	7 days	Improve accountability
Establish staff productivity measures	10 days	Improve productivity
Reassign and/or terminate unnecessary positions	10 days	Improve operational efficiency
Establish temporary pay rate adjustments for physicians and staff	15 days	Reduce monthly expenses
Reduce long-term staffing costs to national benchmark levels	30 days	Reduce operating costs
Develop monthly physician productivity goals	30 days	Increase revenue
Establish regular business management and staff meetings	30 days	Improve communication, cooperation and decision making
Sublet space for new office	60 days	Reduce overhead

FIGURE 2. Action grid for the consultant team.

STAFF ACCOUNTANT		
Action	Deadline	Purpose
Prepare weekly cash flow report	Every Monday	Improve communication of financial position, monitor trends and allow for sound financial planning
Prepare weekly aged receivable report with graphic presentation	Every Monday	Improve communication of financial position, monitor trends and allow for sound financial planning
Prepare monthly graphs • Productivity reports by MD/provider • New and established patient visits by provider • Procedures and deliveries • Referral sources • Accounts receivable management • Payer mix/performance	7th of each month	Improve communication of financial position, monitor trends and allow for sound financial planning
Prepare analytical report on top 10 payers mix and financial performance	30 days	Improve communication of financial position, monitor trends and allow for sound financial planning
Collaborate with interim administrator on financial planning	Once a week	Improve communication of financial position, monitor trends and allow for sound financial planning
Reduce operating expenses and stop capital spending	Immediately	Apply sound financial principles
Negotiate vendor payment terms	Immediately	Reduce financial pressures
Explore options/cost reduction for malpractice, group health and workers' compensation insurance	Immediately	Reduce operating expense
Conduct supply-vendor cost analysis, including group purchasing	15 days	Reduce supply costs
Renegotiate loan payments on capital debt	Immediately	Reduce monthly financial outlay
Prepare practice budget	60 days	Improve financial management

FIGURE 3. Action grid for the staff accountant.

sultant team knew there was hope for the future, and this was the picture we intended to paint.

The first meeting was with the physicians. Once they understood the gravity of the practice's finances, they agreed to a request to reduce their salaries by 10% for six months, with a payback of six equal payments beginning in 24 months. It was further explained that the goal was to have the practice on sound financial footing within 12 to 18 months, so partnership agreements could be pursued. The physicians were promised that they would receive monthly reports to keep them abreast of the practice's financial performance.

The second meeting included the entire staff. In this meeting, we explained the practice's position and the necessity to reassign some positions and lower staffing costs. We asked for people to consider the option of reducing their work hours or volunteering to be furloughed. Immediately following this meeting, each staff member met individually with Dr. Bradford and one of the consultants to discuss his or her own situation and options. We explained that each position would be re-evaluated and structured so that productivity could be measured and we could capitalize on the individual strengths of staff members.

This entire process was difficult and emotional for Dr. Bradford but was essential to move the practice out of the red. Several employees resigned; but for the most part, staff members wanted to support Evergreen Women's Center and were willing to reduce their hours, roll up their sleeves and become part of the solution. This was encouraging.

THE RESULTS

During the three months it took to obtain a top-notch administrator, efforts focused on communication, building a strong infrastructure, accountability and improving finances.

Once the new administrator was in place, progress moved rapidly. Within 12 months, the financial-recovery plan was complete, and the practice was able to begin repayment to the physicians for the initial six-month cut back in pay.

During the implementation of the turnaround, some difficult business decisions were made. These decisions were essential to getting Evergreen Women's Center on solid ground and accomplishing the stated objectives:

• Improved leadership and communication;

- Monthly monitoring of critical financial data;
- Increased collections;
- Debt reduction;
- Improved cash flow;
- Controlled growth;
- Increased physician and staff productivity; and
- Higher physician and staff satisfaction.

The entire recovery process was valuable in teaching all the physicians some sound business principles for managing the practice and monitoring financial performance. Evergreen Women's Center achieved group viability, improved operating performance and financial stability.

The reorganization process also revealed the strengths of many of the employees. Angela Lopez, who rallied to the cause as the project coordinator, became the billing supervisor. She went on to achieve designation as a Certified Medical Manager through the Professional Association of Health Care Office Management and will assume responsibility for managing Evergreen's new satellite office. Other employees also learned a great deal by experiencing the turnaround, gaining confidence and putting their skills to good use at Evergreen Women's Center.

THE NEXT STEP

The old saying "failure to plan is planning to fail" was a reality Evergreen Women's Center didn't want to experience again. Fifteen months after the practice reorganization began, the physicians and management team participated in a strategic planning session. Together, they clarified future goals for the practice and determined the financial resources and strategies required to achieve the stated goals. This was accomplished through market research, demographic analysis and gaining an understanding of Evergreen's market strengths and weaknesses.

The strategic planning process included an examination of potential opportunities within the community to expand the practice and the services Evergreen had to offer. At the same time, it was important to explore potential concerns including what perceived or existing competitors and market conditions might pose a threat to Evergreen's ability to draw on its strengths. Examining these issues was critical to developing a realistic strategic plan. At last, Evergreen Women's Center understood the importance of strategic planning to prepare for the future and guide its actions.

The physicians and the administrator of Evergreen Women's Group closely examined their options before making decisions that would affect their future. In the end, the strategic plan was designed to serve as Evergreen Women's Center's blueprint for the future.

Within 18 months of Dr. Bradford's first call to my office, she was able to offer the other physicians partnership into a practice with a stable future. Evergreen Women's Center now takes a methodical, carefully crafted approach to growth. Their future is more predictable and far more secure.

Evergreen Women's Center is a fine-tuned practice that now stands out from the crowd. Without question, its solid infrastructure, approach to decision making and cautious regard for managing finances makes it a top-performing practice.

The Secrets

1. Uncontrolled growth can result in a loss of control and financial hardship.
2. Strategic planning puts you in charge of your future.
3. A demand for your services does not guarantee your success.
4. Establish reporting methods that help identify red flags in practice performance.
5. Practice finances must be monitored and "managed" before a crisis emerges.
6. Develop a solid infrastructure that supports future growth.
7. Clarify job responsibilities to improve efficiency.
8. Productivity measures improve output.
9. Adding staff is not always the solution to improving output.
10. Prompt action is required to overcome financial problems.
11. Financially plan and budget for practice growth.

FORM ADDED TO YOUR TOOLBOX:

∞ *Sample Organizational Chart: Group OB-GYN Practice* (p. 170)

CHAPTER 11

Reshaping the Practice— A New Genre

W ith not enough money and too many demands upon their time, many physicians with traditional medical practices are looking at ways to improve their practice. They want to serve their patients better, but often struggle with the dynamics of running a medical practice.

> **KEY FACT:** *The physician and administrator are the catalysts for reshaping the practice.*

There is so much pressure and influence from outside the practice—everything from increasingly demanding patients to lower reimbursement rates and a government that scrutinizes doctors and changes the rules. This constant barrage affects the medical practice and choices physicians make.

The physician's goal is to unload these worries and get back to enjoying his or her patients. In this quest, they look for ways to reshape the practice and redirect its focus. Whatever opportunity a physician pursues, whether it's creating a "concierge" type practice, moving toward sports medicine or adding more diverse services, the success of a new genre depends on taking the right approach.

Don't impulsively change your practice. Just because Dr. Marcus down the street starts doing bone density studies or adds a treadmill doesn't mean it's right for your practice to follow suit. Looking for new sources of revenue or ways to improve the practice's services is reasonable, but expanding your services requires careful and deliberate planning.

WHAT DO YOU WANT TO DO?

If you are looking for ways to revamp the practice by attracting different patients, changing the services you provide or adopting a new practice philosophy, you had better look within before you begin. Your commitment is essential. What can you commit to and feel passionate about? In what areas do you excel? In this early assessment stage, concentrate on being honest with yourself and avoiding undue outside influences such as what you think makes financial sense. Focus on your talent and passion. Accurate self-examination is critical to making a successful major transition in what you do and how you do it. An expert in strategic planning can help you avoid making mistakes that might have serious consequences.

DOING IT RIGHT

Start with a commitment to an exploratory process that includes everything from soul-searching and analyzing your strengths to examining what opportunities are available and what makes sense, based on market needs, your talents and what you really want. But don't expect a yellow-brick road that will lead you to your ultimate destination—it's not that simple! You must match the practice's desire and skill sets with existing opportunities. There are a few critical questions you must answer:

1. Is there a demand for the service?
2. Is someone else already providing the service?
3. Who is my competition?
4. Can I do it better than the competition?
5. How will I attract patients?
6. How long will it take to meet my market potential?

Once you decide to move forward, you'll need a solid plan for integrating and marketing the service—whether it's just to your own patients or to a broader market.

If the genre you plan to offer involves a financial commitment, you'll want to conduct a feasibility study to understand the market, analyze your return on investment and project your break-even point. This examination considers your current position in the marketplace and other factors, such as your image in the community, patient attitudes and impact upon staff and operations.

MAKING IT HAPPEN

If you want something in the practice to change, you—the physician and manager—must lead. As the catalyst, your commitment will make the difference. Some physicians come up with their own ideas about something new they can offer their patients. Others simply want to get on board with the latest trend—doing stress testing, DEXA scans, weight management, you name it! These efforts are destined to fail without strong commitment. Here are examples of some of your peers that have successfully made major changes within their practices and reaped the rewards of their commitment.

THE BOUTIQUE PRACTICE

I met with Paul Block, M.D., a previous client of mine in Thousand Oaks, California, one year after he signed on with MDVIP to establish a concierge practice. I asked him why he made such a dramatic shift in his practice model. He told me, "It's all about time! I wanted more time with my patients. It's been a wise decision. I love it and so do they!"

Dr. Block is one of three physicians in a nearly 30-year-old group internal medicine/pulmonary practice. He watched overhead climb and reimbursement decline for more than 10 years. To survive financially, Dr. Block, like physicians across the country, went into survival mode—volume! This meant seeing more patients. He was dissatisfied with this style of medicine and yearned for the "good old days" when physicians knew their patients, patients were loyal and visits were unhurried. He fondly recalled the days when hospital executives and physicians worked without conflicting objectives. By 2004, this just wasn't a reality.

The Reality Check

The demands of patient care have changed dramatically. Thirty years ago, a primary care physician managed less than 1,000 patients; now each manages more than 2,500. Additionally, insurance companies are the primary source for adding new patients to the practice. Physicians are being rushed, and patients are less satisfied.

Self-Examination

For over one year, Dr. Block considered his practice and his motivations and wondered what he could do to get back to the patient care model he enjoyed so much in the 1970s. He had heard about boutique medicine— the concierge-type practice that focuses on specialized care, serving fewer patients and giving each one more time. This concept seemed too good to be true: having enough time with patients to know them as individuals, carefully probe their history and provide a detailed exam without feeling rushed. It sounded like a page from history, but his curiosity and desire to provide better service for his patients drove him to further explore the "boutique" practice model.

Checking It Out

Dr. Block met representatives from MDVIP, a corporation that specializes in helping physicians develop a boutique practice. He learned about its philosophy and methods for converting an established practice to a practice with personalized health care. The success of such a practice requires scaling down the practice, reducing the patient volume to as little as 25% of a typical primary care doctor. This allows the physician to dedicate far more time to each patient. Initial consultations are 90 minutes, and a half-hour is dedicated to acute and follow-up visits. In order to make this system work, patients need to commit to paying for the doctor's time. Since the MDVIP physician dedicates his practice to fewer patients, less than 600, he is more accessible to the patient and can dedicate more time to each of them.

With the MDVIP physician, each patient is charged an annual fee of $1,800 that includes:

- **Preventive care physical exam:** The physical exam is extensive and much more involved than the traditional "comprehensive exam." In Dr. Block's practice, it includes a nutritional evaluation, an activity assessment to examine activities of daily living, a sleep questionnaire, a mini-mental status and depression assessment and a complete examination and assessment. During this visit, Dr. Block dedicates not only the time he needs to conduct the examination, but as much time as the patient needs to get his or her questions answered and be reassured.
- **Comprehensive wellness and lifestyle planning:** It's highly unlikely that physicians in traditional medicine have time to address this in the limited time spent with a patient visit.
- **Personal health record CD-ROM.**

It took Dr. Block more than a year to recognize that this was the niche he was looking for—a way to practice medicine the way it was done in the '70s.

The Transition

Dr. Block decided to move forward. MDVIP's corporate services staff members helped convert the practice by supplying materials and support. They briefed him on what to expect and were available for handholding.

MDVIP sponsored seminars for his patients during the transition and also held a workshop for staff on patient relations. Dr. Block was directed to set up this new practice model and make it truly patient-focused. MDVIP provides on-going support once the practice comes on board. It provides a newsletter and tracks patient outcomes by monitoring emergency room visits and hospitalization.

Reflecting on the Change

"When you are taking care of 2,500 patients, you don't have time to get to know each of them, and it's frustrating. You feel like a hamster in a cage, going round and round. Concierge (boutique) medicine is about time—taking time to give each patient more care and build relationships with your patients— really getting to know each one of them and being there for them whenever they need you." Dr. Block told me when we met, "I'm on call 24/7, and it's fine with me—it's what I want to do to provide the best quality care for my patients." He is also available by email and keeps in close contact with his patients. It seems the patients love this and are willing to pay for it, and according to Dr. Block, it's not the wealthiest patients that sign on.

It has now been a year since Dr. Block became an MDVIP physician. I asked him if he has any regrets. He reflected for a few minutes, looked up and said, "No, this really works for me and for my patients." He is calm, and he is happy. His passion for medicine has been revived.

SHIFTING TO COSMETICS

Plastic reconstructive surgeons are dedicated physicians. Their reconstructive talents are amazing. They transform the lives of people forever by changing the way patients look and feel about themselves. Take the child born with a birth defect that distorts half of his face. The skilled plastic surgeon corrects this so the child looks and feels normal. What about the burn victim who needs multiple plastic surgeries to reconstruct her body? The results are incredible. These are awesome responsibilities. But with the advent of managed care, there's another side to this coin that makes life for the reconstructive surgeon difficult.

The Changing Economics

Medicine is a business, and the insurance companies have hit plastic reconstructive surgeons with this reality. They have ratcheted down the fees they pay for delicate reconstructive surgery and continually scrutinize the need for such services. This often puts the surgeon in the position of having to justify the need for surgery, involving excessive time and reams of paperwork for the physician's staff. With this squeeze put on dedicated plastic reconstructive surgeons, they begin to look at ways to make the practice less vulnerable. Marshall Grainger, M.D., a prominent plastic surgeon, was no exception.

About the Practice

Dr. Grainger called my office in the late 1990s. He had a very busy reconstructive surgery practice in the northwest and particularly enjoyed working with children. He volunteered each year to spend time doing reconstructive surgery in under-developed countries and had earned quite an international reputation. Typically, 75% of his patients required reconstructive surgery, and the remainder had elective cosmetic procedures and paid out-of-pocket. The cosmetic cases were enjoyable, but his first love was reconstructive surgery. Unfortunately, his reconstructive practice was feeling the pinch of managed care—both on staffing needs and financially.

In the previous three years, Dr. Grainger doubled the number of staff members in his insurance department. Meanwhile, reimbursement for reconstructive surgery continued to drop. After 20 years of practice, Dr. Grainger knew he needed to make a shift. He could not do enough reconstructive procedures to make up for lower reimbursement, increased overhead costs and his volunteer work.

Moving In a New Direction

It was time to increase the ratio of cosmetic surgery procedures. For the previous six months, Dr. Grainger had presented several community lectures on cosmetic surgery in an effort to attract more patients. Still, there was little change in the practice mix. I was called in to suggest ways to increase the number of elective procedures.

I spent a day with the practice, interviewing the entire staff and watching as they worked. I examined appointment schedules for past months and the next month. I talked to the manager and the receptionist/scheduler about Dr. Grainger's intent to shift to more cosmetic procedures. Dr. Grainger had indeed told staff members (six months prior) that he wanted to perform more cosmetic procedures and asked Sarah, the receptionist, to be sure and accommodate any patient calling for a cosmetic appointment, but that's as far as it went. No goals were set, and there was little preparation or thought given to how this practice could actually change its patient base.

Digging Deeper

I looked at the statistics on the number of cosmetic versus reconstructive consults that were performed in the office the previous quarter. This revealed a 74/26 ratio—74% were reconstructive patients. When I compared this to the same quarter the prior year, it showed only a slight variation.

The receptionist was probed on her scheduling techniques. This revealed that reconstructive and cosmetic consultations were handled in the same way: The patient would be offered the next available appointment—usually a two- or three-week wait. This wait was longer than desirable for a cosmetic surgery practice. It's important with elective services to expedite getting patients into the office—while they are highly motivated.

The past appointment schedule also showed that 20% of patients scheduled for new cosmetic consultations were not showing up for their appointments. In addition to these no-shows, there were patients that called for an appointment but didn't schedule because the next available appointment was two or three weeks away.

What was Dr. Grainger's staff doing to make this practice cosmetic-patient friendly? Very little! There were six major internal factors that contributed to the lack of growth in cosmetic procedures:

1. The practice did not define specific cosmetic patient goals and time frames to accomplish them.

2. There was no template that reserved a specific number of appointment slots for new cosmetic patients.

3. There were no grouped time slots specifically for cosmetic patients. This resulted in these patients being sandwiched between reconstructive patient appointments—not a good mix, because of the very different needs and attitudes of these two types of patients. Also, dealing with the variables in these patient types requires a different mindset for staff. For example, with patients that need reconstructive surgery, staff must focus on insurance coverage issues and informing patients of the necessary wait to obtain authorization for surgery. With cosmetic patients, the focus is on obtaining a commitment and discussing the costs and payment for services.

TABLE 1. Goals for Increasing Cosmetic Consultations

Time Period	Cosmetic (% of consults)	Reconstructive (% of consults)
4th quarter 1998 (baseline)	26	74
1st quarter 1999	30	70
2nd quarter 1999	40	60
3rd quarter 1999	50	50
4th quarter 1999	60	40

4. There was no post-consult summary to discuss finances, answer questions and schedule the cosmetic surgery.
5. No protocol was in place to record inquiries about cosmetic procedures, eliminating the ability to monitor staff's rate of converting inquiries to patients.
6. There were no tracking tools in place to follow the cosmetic patients.

The physician and staff were too close to the situation to realize they were placing cosmetic patients in a difficult position. Cosmetic patients may be uncomfortable and feel superficial and vain when they wait in the reception room with disfigured patients whose surgical needs are far greater. Cosmetic services are elective, and their visit experience must be positive from the time they first call the office until their consult appointment is complete.

Moving in the Right Direction

To improve Dr. Grainger's cosmetic procedure ratio, we began by establishing sensible growth targets. We used the previous quarter's statistical ratio to develop realistic quarterly goals for shifting the numbers (Table 1).

In order to achieve the established goals, a scheduling template was developed. The template reserved slots specifically for cosmetic patients, and the number reserved was in line with the ratio of cosmetic patients required to meet the quarterly goals. These scheduling slots were concurrent so that specific mornings and afternoons were dedicated to cosmetic patients. This did not interfere with the services provided for reconstructive patients and did not place the cosmetic patient in an uncomfortable position.

Beyond this, with the cosmetic consultations being seen in specific time blocks, the staff members were able to give each patient the attention

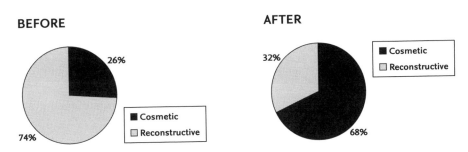

FIGURE 1. Ratio of cosmetic and reconstructive procedures before and after the new measures were adopted.

required. Each cosmetic patient was given a full half hour with the physician, followed by a half hour for computer imaging and consultation with the coordinator of cosmetic services.

The coordinator of cosmetic services managed the cosmetic program as well. When a patient hesitated to schedule a consultation with the scheduler, the call was transferred to the coordinator to increase the conversion rate. She also tracked all inquiries, appointments and procedures through the use of a database enabling patients to receive timely office mailings, including information about upcoming seminars and special events.

The actual numbers were monitored to see if further adjustments were needed down the road, but the practice remained on target and exceeded its goals by the 4th quarter of 1999 (Figure 1).

A World of Difference

Within a year, the conversion rate from inquiry to appointment for cosmetic patients jumped 30%. Beyond this, 75% of these patients scheduled cosmetic surgery. The practice also added a skin center program that sells top-of-the-line skin care products and conducts skin care workshops.

Dr. Grainger has benefited from some wonderful publicity for his work with cosmetic patients, creating additional demand for his services. Since Dr. Grainger has every intention of dedicating at least 25% of his time to reconstructive patients, he has hired a new associate. With a well-trained, dedicated staff, the patients are accepting the new associate and she is building a solid patient base. Dr. Grainger has created the perfect balance to expand the cosmetic genre while continuing the reconstructive and volunteer work that is so important to him.

GOING BARIATRICS

Long before celebrities Al Roker and Carnie Wilson ever thought about gastric bypass surgery, I received a call from Robert Harris, M.D., a young general surgeon that wanted to make this the focus of his practice. Dr. Harris had performed bariatric surgery for several years and was the only surgeon in town doing this procedure. He observed his patients' response closely and was impressed with the way the resulting weight loss changed the health, attitude and quality of life for them. He was committed to continue this work and enthused about making it a major part of his practice.

Dr. Harris hired an advertising specialist and created a slick four-color brochure and an advertising campaign that included community outreach. By the time he contacted me, several months had passed, and he was disappointed with the results. He was performing only three to five gastric bypass surgeries a month, a marginal increase over his pre-marketing days. Something seemed wrong, but he wasn't sure what it was.

The Practice

Dr. Harris ran a typical general surgery practice with three staffers in a 1,400 square foot office. His manager, Marie, ran the front desk and handled all of the phone calls, scheduling, billing and reception duties. The nurse, Anna, had worked with Dr. Harris for the past 12 years and was immersed in the practice. The patients knew and loved her. The third staff person was Chandra, a part-time medical assistant that worked both the front and back office. She cleaned the exam rooms, autoclaved instruments, answered phones and did the filing.

Everyone had a job to do and seemed to manage it with precision. The problem was, they had no idea how to help Dr. Harris build a bariatric practice. They watched the advertising agency come in and out of the office, heard talk about a direct mail campaign, saw bundles of the slick brochure and listened to Dr. Harris talk about doing more gastric bypass surgeries, but they never related this to their jobs or anything concrete. This meant patients that called about gastric bypass were treated like every other patient—there was little procedural difference, other than scheduling their psychological evaluation and pre-surgical history and physical.

Strengthening His Position

My first recommendation to Dr. Harris was to obtain a toll-free phone number specifically for bypass surgery inquiries. This dedicated line, along with bypass surgery inquiries that came into the regular phone line, needed to be fielded by someone in the office whose main focus was gastric bypass patients—answering their questions, scheduling their appointments, participating in their work-up and coordinating their care. It also required providing on-going support for these sometimes-apprehensive patients.

Since Anna, the nurse, had no interest in this type of position and no time to spare, I suggested hiring a nurse educator and training her on all aspects of gastric bypass. The nurse educator would also be responsible for tracking the calls, consultations and number of consultations that resulted in surgical procedures. She would also be the liaison with the advertising agency, coordinating activities and following through on recommendations.

The Nurse Educator

Finding someone to fill the role of nurse educator was not difficult. As in most cases, there were many nurses seeking to move beyond the traditional role of hospital nurse. Twenty-five nurses applied for the position, and we found just the right candidate. Diana was a confident, conscientious, out-going nurse with experience in the operating room and on the surgical floor of the community hospital. She exuded enthusiasm and confidence, and she was an independent worker. To top it off, she had great organizational skills.

With Diana's assistance, I developed protocols on how to handle everything from the first phone call to the patient's one-year follow-up exam and everything in between. Diana went to surgery with Dr. Harris and learned as much as she could about the procedure. She talked with previous patients and met with each of them when they came in for follow-up. She found out what their needs were and learned all about theirs fears. Within six months, Diana developed a support group that was a major hit. Past patients gave testimonials, and people considering surgery came in to gather information and learn more about the procedure—what to expect and how it affected patients. When people called the office to talk about gastric bypass, Diana would give them her full attention and whatever time they needed to get their questions answered.

Contact information for both patients and those who inquired about the procedure were placed in a database. These people received a newsletter and were invited to attend the support group meetings. Within three years, Dr. Harris was known throughout the county for his work in bariatrics and was featured in area newspapers. Some patients were coming from 500 miles away to seek his services.

Within five years, Dr. Harris' practice was limited to bariatric patients. He has proctored other physicians and has gained a national reputation. Diana is still with him, and he contributes his success to her involvement. Dr. Harris is on the cutting edge of change in bariatric procedures and has an incredibly dynamic practice.

OTHER OPPORTUNITIES

There are a multitude of ways physicians can reshape their practices to meet new demands and a changing health care economy. Holistic practices, once thought to be on the edge, are now becoming mainstream. Patients in all parts of the country are seeking physicians that offer complementary and alternative medicine (CAM) services. A number of physicians find that some of these services blend well with their traditional practice. These CAM services not only provide an additional revenue stream to the practice, but they also provide increased convenience for patients.

Travel medicine can be a great practice builder for the primary care physician. There are also weight reduction programs and programs that focus on health and fitness, whether it is sports medicine for the orthopaedic surgeon or nutrition or exercise programs for a variety of specialists. Some OB-GYN practices are expanding their services by looking at the "total woman," by developing wellness and weight management programs.

A forward-thinking OB-GYN practice looking for an additional revenue stream might even consider collaborating with a local gym to offer memberships to patients of the practice. Such a business venture could be expanded to sell products, such as exercise videos, work-out clothing and maternity wear with the practice logo. Pediatricians could easily collaborate with OB-GYN practices in developing "Mommy and Me" and "Preparing for Motherhood" programs.

There are a multitude of ways physicians can expand their practices and better serve both their patients and the community. The opportunities are limited only by the imagination. Of course, physicians must be careful to engage in activities that support their mission and maintain the professional dignity of the practice.

IN THE END

You can change the direction or focus of the practice—whether you want to add or eliminate certain services, appeal to a different consumer or size up or down. If you are committed, dedicate time and resources to explore your options and develop a solid strategic plan, you can create a new genre that defines your future. You have choices: It's your practice, your business.

The Secrets

1. You have choices in reshaping your practice.
2. Respond to the marketplace.
3. Don't feel compelled to mimic your competition or follow the latest fad.
4. Self-examination is vital to successfully changing the services you offer.
5. Plan carefully, and dedicate time and resources to shifting your practice's services.
6. The success of a new genre is rooted in your commitment.

FORMS ADDED TO YOUR TOOLBOX:

∘➥ *Guidelines for Strategic Planning* (p. 171)

CHAPTER 12

The Practice of the Future

W ho can predict how medical practices will function in the future? Certainly not me—I don't have a crystal ball or a stash of fortune cookies in the cupboard, and I don't profess to read palms or tea leaves. Nonetheless, I do believe there are a few obvious changes we can expect to impact medical practices in the near future. These changes center on measuring and managing quality of services and care; focusing on employees' expectations and needs; and advancing the level of technology.

> **KEY FACT:** *Medical executives and physicians can expect changes that will influence their practice in positive and exciting ways.*

THE QUALITY FACTOR

Quality plays an important role in improving outcomes through increased efficiency, reducing errors and controlling the cost of health care. This focus has increased considerably over the past 10 years, and the commitment to improve quality will continue.

There are reports on quality that review safety issues involved with patient care. A study examining patient safety incidents in America's hospitals conducted by HealthGrades reviewed nearly 39 million patient records, applying 13 patient safety indicators. Based on the study, Health-Grades identified 135 hospitals that rated in the top 10% of the nation in terms of patient safety.

The US Department of Health and Human Services Agency for Healthcare Research and Quality prepares an annual report on health care disparity, based on studies involving the quality of and access to health care for different segments of the population.

The National Committee for Quality Assurance (NCQA), a private, not-for-profit organization is dedicated to improving health care quality. The NCQA provides quality oversight and improvement initiatives at all levels of the health care system. The quality of health care discussed in a report prepared by the NCQA based on performance data from health plans, *The State of Health Care Quality*, revealed that performance on key measures of clinical quality has improved in recent years, a promising trend and one that is expected to continue.

The NCQA states that it is not coincidental that the latest performance gains were recorded in a year that saw broad acceptance of two important and complementary improvement strategies: paying for quality and physician- and hospital-level performance measurement. These two strategies have been incorporated into mainstream efforts to improve care and prevent complications. The pay-for-performance concept approaches offering incentives based on performance. The incentives can be financial or the promise of added recognition in a provider directory. These efforts are diverse, ranging from government-sponsored to health-plan-specific initiatives.

NCQA's new Quality Plus standards are designed to recognize and reward leading edge organizations that meet tough new standards in the areas of Member Connections, and Care Management & Health Improvement. These standards focus on promoting wellness and prevention.

Health insurers also have internal programs to measure quality and identify physicians that provide higher quality (i.e., access to care, continuity of care, utilization, patient satisfaction, outcomes). They develop their own report cards and gather data from various sources including claims and patient surveys.

These are just a few of the sources that are reviewing and analyzing health care quality and looking at different performance measures. The focus on quality is obvious and promises to be even more prominent in the future.

Patient satisfaction is moving to the forefront. According to Robert Wolosin of Press Ganey, a consulting firm that specializes in health care satisfaction measurement and improvement, in his article "Role of Patient Satisfaction" in the December 2003 edition of *Physician's News Digest*, "analysts expect greater attention and scrutiny to be given to the accountability function of patient satisfaction scores, and to ways in which patient satisfaction measurement can be further integrated into an overall measure of clinical quality." For some time now, a number of HMOs have rewarded physician groups using health outcomes and patient satisfaction information.

Patients are also beginning to conduct research when choosing their physicians. They go online and seek information about a specific physician through a search engine. They also check out doctors by going to the medical practice's website. Beyond this, patients are able to look at a physician's past performance by obtaining a report, such as the Physician Quality Report produced by HealthGrades and available with the click of a mouse.

These studies and actions are all evidence of a continued and growing commitment to improve health care quality. This includes an increased focus on the expectations of health care providers and establishing sound techniques that address increased accountability.

Physicians and administrators need to establish methods to monitor quality within the medical office. It's not enough to say quality is a priority, it must be demonstrated by integrating quality performance measures into the medical practice. According to Bryan P. Bergeron, M.D., in an article entitled "Performance Management in Small Practices" in the March/April 2005 issue of the *Journal of Medical Practice Management*, "Someone in the practice must decide which indicators to monitor; establish acceptable ranges of indicator values; analyze the data; and act on their analysis. The very process of making these decisions is a major component of performance management." He further states, "It's important to use a mix of clinical and non-clinical indicators to assure inevitable clinical problems are addressed."

In the future, quality measurements will continue to expand beyond the clinical aspects of the practice and examine business practices as well. Office operations must be evaluated, and practices need to commit to reducing processes, eliminating waste and duplication and reducing errors. These are important factors in controlling the costs of running a medical practice. Improvements in quality provide an added advantage of increasing patient, staff and physician satisfaction. Demonstrated quality will also influence a medical group's ability to remain competitive. Physicians that make the commitment to quality and exhibit that commitment can be a driving force in improving the quality of health care services.

FOCUS ON EMPLOYEES

When Generation X and Generation Y entered the workforce, they forever changed the way physician leaders, administrators and office managers think about human resources. These employees have wants and needs that are broader than those of employees of the past. They have different expectations and sometimes question authority. They want to know why something must be done a certain way and need to be convinced before they willingly accept change. These employees present new challenges and expect managers to earn their loyalty.

Large corporations have resources to analyze these differences and explore ways to meet the needs of new generations of employees. Smaller employers, such as medical practices, compete for these employees without the resources of big industry. I believe physicians and administrators will face continued challenges in their efforts to recruit and retain skilled and dedicated employees. It may require expanding the realm of what they offer for employees.

Medical practices can explore possibilities that are mutually beneficial. For example, the practice can offer preventive health programs on site and partially pay the membership dues for staff to join a local health club. By doing this, the practice becomes a more competitive employer and will encourage a healthier staff, which may in the end affect its health care insurance premiums. It also happens to provide an endorsement of the practice's commitment to better health. This is just one example of what might be expected in the future. Business managers will continually seek ways to unite with employees in a meaningful way that improves business performance and places increased value on employees.

Simple steps to providing an employee-friendly work environment can also be found in Laura Sachs Hills' book *"How to Recruit, Motivate and Manage a Winning Staff,"* (Greenbranch Publishing, 2004). It's an excellent source of helpful, practical tips on things physicians and administrators can do to show employees they recognize the value these employees bring to the practice.

Information technology also changes what we need and expect from employees. The medical practice already dependent on its computer will find its needs and usage expanding. Beyond collecting and moving data electronically, it will be called upon to store and manage even more data as it moves through the age of technology. Some medical practices have already prepared for this by creating a key position of Management Information Systems (MIS) Manager, or for the smaller practice an MIS Coordinator. The medical office of the future must have as its internal point person someone with a keen understanding of the practice's MIS—someone that assumes responsibility for keeping the systems up and running and managing the electronic information.

Physician employees

A shift from physician ownership to physician employee is a continuing trend. According to Pamela L. Moore in the article "Can We All Get Along? Bridging the Generation Gap," appearing in the May/June 2001 issue of *Physicians Practice*. "An increasing number of physicians are working their first jobs employed in a group practice or hospital; they aren't starting up a fledging one- or two-doc practice, as their predecessors did." The article quotes John Potter, chief executive at Dreyer Medical Group in Aurora, Ill. "Junior docs see medicine as a job with hours, and then they're off."

It is true, the new generation of physicians do not feel the practice is their life. Employed physicians—and younger physicians in general—will continue to change the dynamics of the medical practice. It will be a challenge to balance all the needs of the practice and patients with the wants and needs of these young physicians. If these needs are not balanced, practices may be faced with costly physician retention issues.

ADVANCING TECHNOLOGY

The evolution of technology in the medical practice has a long way to go, but has limitless potential. Physicians and administrators are exploring new options and investing in technology that will move them into the future. The electronic health record (EHR), sometimes referred to as the electronic medical record, is a basic but perfect example. Physicians, somewhat hesitant to adopt the EHR in the past, are now declaring this a must. Switching to EHRs provides a powerful tool to help medical practices extract, analyze and manage data. It's an integral part of evidence-based medicine, reducing errors, measuring quality and building accountability into the health care system not only for providers, but to ensure patients are compliant, which can contribute significantly to improving quality.

Technology has made major advancements through the development of diagnostic tools, resulting in early detection. Computers and advanced technology are also changing the way physicians perform surgery, making procedures safer and less invasive. Some surgeons are now completing surgical procedures with the use of a surgical cart—the robot—while seated at a console viewing three-dimensional images of the surgical area of the patient. This is just the beginning of how technology will advance the field of medicine and change how health care professionals are trained, how they are evaluated and what they must do to keep their skills current.

Medical residents are now learning both cognitive and surgical techniques in a way unimaginable 15 years ago. It is expected that advancements in technology will continue to change the training of future physicians and improve outcomes. The operating room of the future is not likely to resemble those from the past.

Technology will permeate the medical practice of the future, from how business aspects are managed to the quality of care provided to patients. Patients that in the past needed to obtain their medical records from multiple sources will eventually have access to an electronic copy of their complete health record. This record will follow them through the health care system, regardless of where they seek medical care.

Technology moves information accurately and swiftly—at a speed that increases demand and changes expectations. Technology leads the way in improving precision with both clinical and business processes. It's the wave of the future, and the future is here!

ONE STEP AT A TIME

The future of the medical practice may not be predictable, but it is guaranteed to be exciting. These are revolutionary times for physicians and health care executives.

The focus on quality, a new and different employee workforce and the rapid advancement of technology will change the outlook of the medical practice, but it's still a matter of looking ahead and moving forward one step at a time. The real secret to your success is welcoming the future and embracing the opportunities it has to offer.

The Secrets

1. The nation's focus on health care quality is a reality.

2. Health care quality has both clinical and nonclinical components.
3. A commitment to health care quality must be demonstrated within the medical practice.
4. Maintaining loyal and dedicated employees requires more effort than in the past.
5. Technology is a major contributor to improving efficiency.
6. Technology advancements play an important role in mastering clinical skills.
7. The future is changing; but with the changes, far more opportunities emerge.
8. These are revolutionary times.

FORM ADDED TO YOUR TOOLBOX:
☞ *Patient Satisfaction Survey* (p. 172)

TOOLBOX FORMS

Chapter 1:
- Sample Job Description: Receptionist

Chapter 2:
- Telephone Appointment Tracking
- Clinical Telephone Tracking
- Patient Visit Time Study

Chapter 3:
- Training Monitor
- The Art of Delegation

Chapter 4:
- Appointment Power Words Matrix
- Rooming Matrix

Chapter 5:
- Communication Matrix
- Tracking Log Diagnostic Studies
- Sample Discharge Letter

Chapter 6:
- Physician's Retreat Questionnaire
- Team Leader Tips

Chapter 7:
- Risk/Opportunity Matrix
- Sample Performance Standards Worksheet

Chapter 8:
- Payer Performance Table

Chapter 9:
- Sample Bio Sketch
- Meeting Action Matrix
- Staff Survey: How Does Management Rate?
- Management Skills Audit

Chapter 10:
- Sample Organizational Chart: Group OB-GYN Practice

Chapter 11:
- Guidelines for Strategic Planning

Chapter 12:
- Patient Satisfaction Survey

SAMPLE JOB DESCRIPTION: RECEPTIONIST

Qualifications:
1. High school graduate or GED
2. Keyboard proficiency at 45 wpm
3. Two years medical office experience
4. One year customer service, reception experience
5. One year operating medical office computerized billing system

Personality and Work Traits: Position requires an individual with an enthusiastic and congenial personality that is eager to please. Interpersonal skills are essential. Superior communication skills are necessary, both verbal and non-verbal. Organizational and multi-tasking skills are required. Must be accurate and detail oriented. Able to read, understand and follow oral and written instructions

General Responsibilities:
1. Greet and receive patients and visitors
2. Assist patient with immediate needs and address pertinent questions
3. Coordinate patient activity in reception area, report problems or irregularities, and communicate delays to patients
4. Obtain detailed patient information and copies of insurance card
5. Register new patients on computer system
6. Update patient demographics at each visit
7. Inform patients of the patient payment requirements for their visit
8. Maintain open communication and support customer service needs
9. Oversee reception area maintenance
10. Confirm patient appointments
11. Process daily mail
12. Send out new patient welcome kits and referral thank you notes
13. Other duties as assigned

Typical Physical Demands: Work may require sitting, viewing and operating a computer for long periods of time, as well as stooping, bending and stretching for files and supplies. Manual dexterity required to operate telephone and other small office equipment. Vision must be correctable to 20/20 and hearing must be in a normal range for telephone and direct patient contacts. Job requires occasional lifting, up to 30 lbs.

Direct Report: Operations Supervisor

TELEPHONE APPOINTMENT TRACKING

Week of: _____   **For Dr.** _____

Time Patient Called	Monday	Tuesday	Wednesday	Thursday	Friday	Total Quantity
8:30 – 9:30						
9:30 – 10:30						
10:30 – 11:30						
11:30 – 12:30						
12:30 – 1:30						
1:30 – 2:30						
2:30 – 3:30						
3:30 – 4:30						
4:30 – 5:30						
Total quantity:						
Total quantity voice mail calls:						

If phone calls are not taken during lunch break, please indicate the hours you are not receiving calls:

From _____   **To** _____

CLINICAL TELEPHONE TRACKING: INCOMING CALLS

Date: _____ Day of Week: _____

Physician: _____ Nurse: _____

Time Frame	Insurance Co. Query	Med Probs/ Test Results	Rx	Other MDs/ Hosp	Other
8:00 – 9:00 a.m.					
9:00 – 10:00 a.m.					
10:00 –11:00 a.m.					
11:00 a.m. – noon					
noon – 1:00 p.m.					
1:00 – 2:00 p.m.					
2:00 – 3:00 p.m.					
3:00 – 4:00 p.m.					
4:00 – 5:00 p.m.					
5:00 – 6:00 p.m.					
6:00 – 7:00 p.m.					
Total # of calls					

PATIENT VISIT TIME STUDY

Date _____   Patient _____

Appointment time _____   (circle): New / Estab. Dr. _____

Document <u>exact time</u> and initial for each of the following activities:

1. Patient Arrival _____   Check-in complete _____

2. Patient Roomed _____   Doctor In _____ Doctor Out _____

3. Studies or Lab: List _____

_____

4. Schedule outside studies: Start _____   Finish _____

5. Complete in-house studies: Start _____   Finish _____

6. Arrive at check-out _____   Complete check-out _____

Record reason for delays, key by number assigned to descriptor:

TRAINING MONITOR

Employee Name _____   Position _____

Trainer _____   Department _____

Week of _____   New Hire _____   Reposition _____   Procedural Change _____

Tasks	Date objectives reviewed	Date task demonstrated	Number of practice sessions	Date of evaluation	Competency rating	Trainer to initial at completion
1						
2						
3						
4						
5						

THE ART OF DELEGATION

DO	DON'T
When delegating a task, select someone you have confidence in.	Do not assign the task to someone that lacks the training or skills to accomplish the assignment.
Be practical and smart.	Don't select an individual that does not have time to do the task.
Delegate challenging tasks that provide an opportunity for growth.	Be careful not to pass work on that is always beneath the person's talent or select one person for all the "undesirable" tasks (things that no one wants to do).
Assign the task to a "specific" individual and set a specific time frame to accomplish it.	Don't get general and suggest that one of the nurses do the task "when you have time."
Tell the person the end result expected. The objective! For example; You want to explore and compare costs for replacing your EKG machine and what features you would like on the new equipment.	Avoid attempts to over manage the project by telling the individual how to accomplish it. Give the expected result and leave the means to him or her.
Obtain feedback from the individual including project objective and time frame for completion.	Don't fail to obtain a commitment
Mark the calendar with the deadline and hold the person accountable for completing the assignment.	Never let the deadline slide. This will send a message that it's not important and the individual can ignore future assignments.
Hold the individual accountable for the outcome.	Don't neglect the outcome. Meeting deadlines is not good enough. If the task is not completed and the objective is not met, require the person to finish it rather than have someone pick up where the first person left off.
Reinforce and give credit for a job well done. If it could have been done better, thank the individual and simply give constructive feedback in a sensitive manner.	As long as the objective has been accomplished, don't be over critical of the outcome or the person's confidence will wane and he or she won't be motivated to accept assignments the next time around.

APPOINTMENT POWER WORDS MATRIX—
A GUIDE TO MANAGING APPOINTMENTS

Activity	What Not to Say	What to Say
Confirming appointments	Let me know if you can't make it. *Message: We know you might not make it and that's okay.*	We're expecting you. We've dedicated this appointment to you. *Rationale: Strong words reinforce the patient's obligation.*
Booking an appointment	I'm squeezing you in. *Message: You'll never be missed if you don't show up or expect to wait when you get here.*	I have an opening for you at 3 p.m. *Rationale: We have time for you and want to see you.*
Calling the no show appointment	I'm calling to reschedule the appointment you missed. *Message: Missed appointment are not your responsibility*	We're concerned that you missed an appointment. It's important that you come in. *Rationale: Emphatic, but empathetic.*
When a patient calls to cancel	Did you want to reschedule the appointment? *Message: It's okay with us if you change appointments at any time.*	It's really important that you keep the appointment. The time is reserved, and doctor would like to see you then. *Rationale: The appointment is important and so are you.*
When you are behind schedule	I'm sorry we're running a little late. *Message: We don't have a handle on our schedule, and we're rushed.*	Doctor needed more time then expected with a couple of our patients. I apologize for the delay. *Rationale: We give patients the time they need, but don't like to keep you waiting.*
When you need to reschedule a patient's appointment	Doctor has to cancel your appointment. *Message: We're more important than you or your time.*	Unfortunately we need to move your appointment. When would be a convenient time for you to come in? *Rationale: "Need" implied changing the appointment could not be avoided. Your technique for rescheduling lets the patient know that you don't want to inconvenience them.*
When the doctor enters the exam room	Why are we seeing you today? *Message: You don't even know why I'm here or what my problems are.*	I understand you've had a cough and chills for the last three days. *Rationale: You've read my chart, and you're going to help me.*

ROOMING MATRIX
Patient Prep Standards

Reason for visit	Ht	Wt	BP	Temp	Resp	Gown	Expose Area	Meds	Aller-gies	Collect Urine
Annual exam	X	X	X	X	X	Full		X	X	
Pre-employ	X	X	X	X	X	Full			X	X
Chief complaint			X	X			X			
• Sore throat			X	X		Upper		X	X	
• Earache			X	X				X	X	
• Respiratory or Cardiac		X	X	X	X	Upper		X	X	
• Dermatology			X	X			X		X	
• Repeat Pap smear		X				Lower				
• Urinary itch or burning				X		Lower			X	X
• Breast check		X	X	X		Upper				
• Vomiting or diarrhea		X	X	X	X	Full		X	X	

COMMUNICATION MATRIX

- Don't blame
- Be neutral
- Ask questions
- Be positive
- Ask for a commitment

- Involve them in the solution
- Be empathetic—show concern
- Be flexible—open minded
- Be personal—use their
  name frequently

Words That Work	Words that DON'T Work!
I, we, it, there, let's	You, can't, should, No

Right Way	Wrong Way
"I think we can work this out"	"You can't do it that way"
"It seems a mistake was made"	"You made a mistake"
"Let's do it this way"	"You should do it this way"
"Tell me how that happened"	"Why did you do that?"
"This is what I can do for you (offer alternatives)"	"No, I can't do that"
"There are some restrictions we need to address"	"You're restricted"
"So, we agree this is how to proceed"	"You have to do it this way"
"I appreciate your concern"	"I know you have a problem"

TRACKING LOG: DIAGNOSTIC STUDIES

Patient's Name	Study	Where per-formed	Date ordered/ scheduled	Date report rec'd	Action/date	Init.
Jane Wells	Biopsy	ABC Pathology	3/2/05	3/9/05	Dr. called patient 3/10/05	jc

SAMPLE DISCHARGE LETTER

Note: Once you develop your form letter, ask your medical malpractice insurance representative to review it.

Date

Dear (Patient):

I find it necessary to advise you that I will no longer be able to provide medical care for you because (describe the reason in objective terms).

Since your condition requires continued medical care, I urge you to seek another physician without delay. At your request, I will be available for emergency care and already scheduled appointments until (give specific date, 30 days from the date this letter is written).

This will give you ample time to select a physician of your choice from the many competent doctors in this area. If you need assistance in selecting a physician, you may want to call the (county) medical society at (phone number) or the local hospital.

I am enclosing an authorization requesting release of your medical records to the physician of your choice. The records will be forwarded upon receipt of your request.

Sincerely yours,

Signature

(Physician's name)

PHYSICIAN'S RETREAT QUESTIONNAIRE

Instructions: Each doctor is asked to complete this confidential survey *and return it to our office at least one week prior to the scheduled retreat.* If additional space is needed, key your response by number and complete on reverse side.

Name: _____   Board Specialty: _____

Date you joined the practice _____

1. What is your description of the practice's mission / purpose?

2. What are **your** three reasons for being with this group (list no more than three)?

3. What different reasons do you think the **other physicians** may have?

4. What do you see as the major strengths you contribute to the practice?

5. What behaviors or actions by other physicians, in prior or current situations, are problematic for you? Please explain.

6. In the following series of questions, please mark your answers on a scale of 0 to 10 indicating your position on each statement, with (0) being NO or NOT VERY and (10) being YES or VERY.

```
     0    1    2    3    4    5    6    7    8    9    10
    (No)                (Somewhat)              (Yes)
```

a.) How interested are you in working in a larger medical group?

```
     0    1    2    3    4    5    6    7    8    9    10
```

b.) Are you willing to seek a workable solution to deal with managed care?

```
     0    1    2    3    4    5    6    7    8    9    10
```

c.) Do you feel that working in a larger group requires sharper communication skills?

```
     0    1    2    3    4    5    6    7    8    9    10
```

d) How important to you is recognition and prestige in your medical community?

```
     0    1    2    3    4    5    6    7    8    9    10
```

e) Are you interested in active participation (leadership) in the business and administrative aspects of the practice?

```
     0    1    2    3    4    5    6    7    8    9    10
```

f.) How important are the following to you at this time?

Stable/increased income	0	1	2	3	4	5	6	7	8	9	10
Benefits and perks	0	1	2	3	4	5	6	7	8	9	10
Independent decision making	0	1	2	3	4	5	6	7	8	9	10
Marketing your practice	0	1	2	3	4	5	6	7	8	9	10
More time for CME	0	1	2	3	4	5	6	7	8	9	10
Expanding patient base	0	1	2	3	4	5	6	7	8	9	10

Participation in business aspects of practice	0	1	2	3	4	5	6	7	8	9	10
Vacation time	0	1	2	3	4	5	6	7	8	9	10
Autonomy	0	1	2	3	4	5	6	7	8	9	10
Days off per week	0	1	2	3	4	5	6	7	8	9	10
Decrease work load	0	1	2	3	4	5	6	7	8	9	10
Time with family	0	1	2	3	4	5	6	7	8	9	10
Sports and hobbies	0	1	2	3	4	5	6	7	8	9	10
Community service	0	1	2	3	4	5	6	7	8	9	10
Religious activities	0	1	2	3	4	5	6	7	8	9	10

7. How big do you expect the group to be three years from now and over what geographic area?

8. Please list or describe your <u>professional</u> goals:
   a.) Short-Term (next 18 months)

   b.) Long-Term (next three years)

9. Please describe or list your <u>personal</u> goals:
   a.) Short-Term

   b.) Long-Term

10. Do you anticipate any lifestyle changes that will affect your ability to maintain your current level of commitment to the practice (i.e. marriage, children, caring for elderly parents, children in college, getting a teaching appointment, taking an administrative position, retirement, etc.)? (yes / no)_____ If yes, what do you see as the impact of these changes?

11. Any comments about the motivations or compatibilities between physicians in the group?

TEAM LEADER TIPS

ACTIONS
1. **Give** capable people a clear idea of the results you want to achieve but leave the methods to them.
2. **Suggest** methods rather than dictating them—with the understanding that they are free to do something better.
3. **Consult** the people affected by a problem or change and ask for their input.
4. **Enrich** jobs by delegating decisions.
5. **Guide** your staff to think of constructive suggestions.
6. **Eliminate** needless rules and allow staff freedom.
7. **Praise** should accompany criticism.
8. **Recognize** why teams fail.

COMMUNICATION
Sensing Statements
   I don't hear any disagreement with Mary's points. Do we all agree?
Thinking Statements
   There seems to be a correlation between the number of lost patients and the increase in patient complaints.
Feeling Statements
   I'm disappointed that we haven't progressed further.
Statement of Intention
   My question is not a criticism, I simply need more information.
Statement of Action
   Let's try cycle billing for a couple of months and see if it improves cash flow.

WHY TEAMS FAIL
✔ Lack of confidence (in either the leader or the team)
✔ Lack of trust
✔ Lack of buy-in
✔ Competing priorities
✔ Poor attitude
✔ Insecurity

WHY TEAMS SUCCEED
✔ Clear objectives
✔ Reasonable expectations
✔ Communication
✔ Coordination and cooperation

RISK/OPPORTUNITY MATRIX

Recommendation	Risk	Opportunity	Economic Impact
Implement strategies to reduce missed appointments to <15%	Change in procedure. Staff resistance	Capture additional revenue	Reduce down-time Estimated at $800,000 additional revenue the first year
Establish benchmarks for improved access	Requires physician commitment to clinic services	Improve patient care services and customer satisfaction	Unknown
Implement a written dispute-resolution process and assign accountability to one source	Short-term investment for long term return	Improve customer service Reduce exposure to malpractice	Unknown

PERFORMANCE STANDARDS WORKSHEET

Description/Activity	Quantity (average: daily/weekly/monthly)	Quality Measurement
Sample 1: Answer incoming phone calls	90–120	Average response time <3 rings 90% of the time
Sample 2: Minimal abandonment of calls	<5%	Average time before call abandoned < 2 minutes 95% of the time

Name _____ Position_____ Date_____

Description/Activity	Quantity (average: daily/ weekly/monthly)	Quality Measurement

PAYER PERFORMANCE TABLE: Reimbursement per CPT Code

CPT Code:	New-Patient Visits			Established-Patient Visits				Office Consultations			*Hassle Factor
	99203	99204	99205	99212	99213	99214	99215	99243	99244	99245	
Ins. Co. 1											
Ins. Co. 2											
Ins. Co. 3											
Ins. Co. 3											
Ins. Co. 4											
Ins. Co. 5											
Ins. Co. 6											

*Hassle factor ratings should be one point for each indicator for a maximum of four points. The more points, the worse the performance. Zero is the best rating.

Hassle factor indicators:
- ✓ Require repeated requests for referral or authorization
- ✓ Slow down in claims processing
- ✓ Patients complain about their insurance company
- ✓ Provider relations support is sub-standard

SAMPLE BIO SKETCH

MEET OUR NEWEST ADDITION!

Please welcome Rachel Taylor to our staff.

Rachel Taylor

Rachel has lived in Tampa since she was seven years old and can't imagine living anywhere else. She married her high school sweetheart, Andrew, while attending Loyola University. They have two teenage children.

For the past five years, Rachel has been managing the billing department of a large MSO. She is excited about joining Mitchell OB-GYN and meeting every one of you. Rachel has missed working in a group practice where she interacts with staff, physicians and patients on a daily basis

Rachel is active in the local PAHCOM chapter and is a certified coder through the American Academy of Professional Coders. She has been a lecturer at their regional meetings and teaches a coding class at a local junior college.

Rachel and Andrew love water sports and were on a championship rowing team two years in a row. They are members of the Sierra Club and have hiked through many of the region's National Parks. Samuel, the family's golden retriever, joins them when they jog through local parks. They are committed to their community and are active in local affairs and their local church, where Rachel has taught Sunday school for the past four years.

We understand Rachel is a chocoholic and has an irresistible passion for The Cheesecake Factory's truffles and hot fudge sundaes.

We look forward to having Rachel as our Assistant Business Manager when she joins us on October 1st. She is a welcome addition to Mitchell OB-GYN.

MEETING ACTION MATRIX

Type of Meeting _____ Date _____

Description/ Action Item	Responsible Party	Target Date	Actual Date	Comments

STAFF SURVEY: How Does Management Rate?

Your perception of how this practice is managed is important to us. We value your opinion and ask you to complete this questionnaire so that we can develop a better understanding of the work environment and each staff member's level of satisfaction.

Please put the completed survey in a sealed envelope and place it on the office manager's or physician's desk within 24 hours. If you answer No to any of the first 10 questions, please explain your answers on the reverse side. Thank you for taking the time to give us your opinions.

	Yes	Some-times	No
1. Does management seem to care about how you feel about your work?			
2. Is management open and honest in dealing with employees?			
3. Do you feel you can go to your immediate supervisor for support and solutions?			
4. Does your manager give you a clear understanding of what is expected of you?			
5. Are you eager to come to work?			
6. Are employees and employer equally loyal, trustworthy and respectful?			
7. Is the office environment between employees and employer comfortable?			
8. Do you receive enough information to perform your work?			
9. Is the supervision you receive adequate?			
10. Do you receive appropriate feedback on your job performance?			

11. How well do you know what is expected of you in your job?
    ____ I know exactly.
    ____ I have a very good idea.
    ____ I have a pretty good idea.
    ____ I have a somewhat vague idea.
    ____ I have only a very vague idea.

12. How sincere is your supervisor's interest in getting your opinions and suggestions?

_____ My supervisor has a very sincere interest in my opinion.

_____ My supervisor has a considerable interest in my opinion.

_____ My supervisor has some interest in my opinion.

_____ My supervisor has little or no interest in my opinion.

_____ I don't know whether my supervisor is interested in my opinion.

13. What do you believe is the current level of employee morale in the practice?

_____ Very high

_____ High

_____ Medium

_____ Low

_____ Very low

14. Why do you believe morale is at this level?

15. What, if anything, could be done to improve morale?

Share your ideas on how to improve your job and/or the practice's operations. (Use additional paper if necessary.)

MANAGEMENT SKILLS AUDIT:
Self-Examination of Management Behavior and Skills

DO YOU:

1. Clarify job expectations and focus on desired outcomes?

2. Encourage and listen to questions and input from others?

3. Encourage employees to give feedback?

4. Communicate matters affecting employees' job, work unit and the organization in an open, honest and TIMELY manner?

5. Conduct timely annual performance evaluations?

6. Treat employees with dignity and respect?

7. Deal promptly and effectively with problem employees?

8. Support employees' development and growth?

9. Recognize and reward superior performance?

10. Coach and help employees learn how to solve problems?

11. Delegate tasks that can easily be done by someone with less expertise than you?

12. Help employees seek opportunities to improve work processes?

13. Share the glory and give credit to employees for contributing to making a better work environment/practice?

14. Take advantage of each employee's strengths?

15. Hire the right employees?

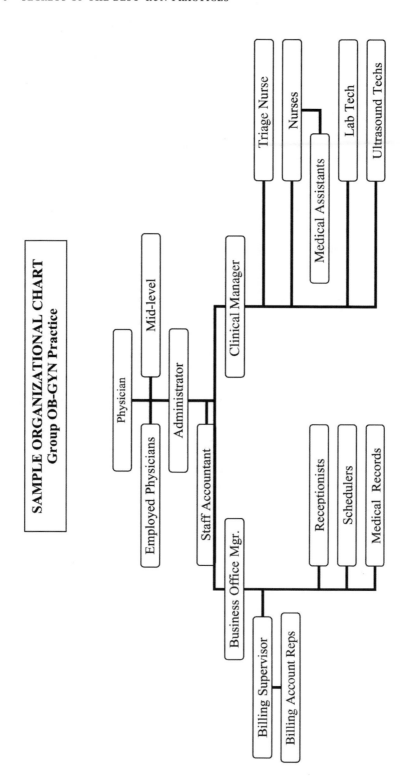

SAMPLE ORGANIZATIONAL CHART
Group OB-GYN Practice

GUIDELINES FOR STRATEGIC PLANNING

Summary: The process of developing a strategic plan requires a SWOT analysis; the assessment of the practice's strengths, weaknesses, opportunities and threats; a self examination and an analysis of the marketplace. The purpose of the strategic plan is to guide the practice's growth, strengthen its position and implement strategies that support its strategic goals.

Conduct practice and market research and analysis

1. Strengths and Opportunities
   a. Determine what the practice does well
   b. Explore untapped talents and resources
   c. Identify specific areas of interest
   d. Identify marketplace needs
   e. Determine target market
   f. Analyze market demographics
   g. Assess patient demographics
2. Weakness and Threats
   a. Examine areas of under performance
   b. Assess practice limitations
   c. Examine market conditions and variables
   d. Identify existing and potential competitors

Conduct strategic retreat

1. Involve all stakeholders
2. Review SWOT analysis
3. Clarify mission
4. Reach agreement
   a. Determine practice's short and long term goals
   b. Identify and commit to specific strategies required to achieve goals
   c. Commit funds and resources required for implementation

Prepare written strategic plan

1. Summarize mission and goals
2. Prepare final list of targets and strategies
3. Assign responsibilities
4. Develop a time line
5. Determine measurements and tracking system

Implementation

1. Involve all stake holders
2. Communicate with entire staff
3. Monitor progress and track results
4. Manage the budget
5. Know when to shift strategies
6. Celebrate your successes

PATIENT SATISFACTION SURVEY

We strive to provide a high level of customer satisfaction. Please help us by evaluating our performance at the time of your last encounter. This will help us understand whether or not we are meeting your needs.

Date of last appointment _____ **Physician** _____

Please answer the following questions to rate your level of satisfaction with the service we provide. Circle one number on each line: Poor = 1, Acceptable = 2, Good = 4, Excellent = 5.

	Poor ←———→ Excellent			
1. Ease of reaching our office on the telephone	1	2	3	4
2. The length of wait time to get into our office for appointment	1	2	3	4
3. The convenience of our office location	1	2	3	4
4. Length of time waiting at the office	1	2	3	4
5. Friendliness of our business office and reception staff	1	2	3	4
6. Friendliness of our nursing staff	1	2	3	4
7. Time spent with the physician	1	2	3	4
8. Explanation of your condition and treatment	1	2	3	4
9. The thoroughness and competence of the physician	1	2	3	4
10. The outcome of your medical care (how you were helped)	1	2	3	4
11. The comfort and cleanliness of our office	1	2	3	4
12. Our staff's regard for your confidentiality and privacy	1	2	3	4
13. If you have the opportunity, will you recommend our office to family and friends?	1	2	3	4

Comments and/or recommendations:

Name (optional):

Index

Page numbers followed by "f" denote figures; those followed by "t" denote tables.

A

A/R. *See* Accounts receivable management
Abandonment, 51
Absenteeism, 60
Academic culture, 62. *See also* Outpatient academic practices
Accounts receivable (A/R) management, 88–90
   aging accounts, 89–90
   third-party reimbursement analysis, 88–89
ACMPE (American College of Medical Practice Executives), 54
Administrative secretaries, of outpatient academic practices, 63
Agency for Healthcare Research and Quality, 139
Aging accounts, 89–90
American Academy of Professional Coders, 105
American College of Medical Practice Executives (ACMPE), 54
Americans with Disabilities Act, 69
Annual physical exams, 30, 31, 32f, 37, 38
Appointment Power Words Matrix: a Guide to Managing Appointments, 154
Appointments, 29–39. *See also* Scheduling
   for annual exams, 30, 31, 32f, 37, 38
   confirmation of, 36, 154
   for cosmetic surgery consultations, 131–133, 132t
   demand vs. capacity for, 30, 34–35
   double-booking, 30, 31, 36
   for established patients, 31, 32f
   financial impact of unmanaged system for, 32–33, 33t
   follow-up, scheduling during check-out process, 26
   for new patients, 31, 32f
      by multiple physicians at the same time, 17, 18
      staggering of, 19
      time required for, 17
   no-shows and cancellations, 30, 31, 34, 38
      for faculty practices, 67–68
      financial impact of, 32, 36
      management of, 35–36

objectives of scheduling system for, 33–34
patient satisfaction with system for, 38
physician arrival in room after scheduled time of, 17
for pre-employment physicals, 31, 32f
problems with scheduling system for, 29–30
   analysis of, 30–32
telephone calls for, 16–20, 29
   hours of, 17
   by schedulers, 18, 19
   time required for, 16–17
   volume of, 16–17
time allotted for, 31
types of, 31, 32f, 34–35, 34t
waiting time for, 29–30, 38
   in outpatient academic practices, 65
work-ins, 30, 31, 32
Art of Delegation, The, 153
Attitudes
about risk management, 52
poor, 7–8, 108
Audits
chart, 18, 46, 82–83
management skills, 169
payroll records, 92
Automated charge reporting, 80
Automated check-writing system, 91

B

Bad attitudes, 7–8, 108
Bank lockbox, 92
Bank statements, 92
Bariatric surgery practice, 134–136
Benefits for employees, 104–105, 142
Best run practices, 1–5
challenges facing, 3, 5
common traits of, 3–5
Billing, 81–82
cash flow problems related to, 113–114
cost of mailing patient statements, 87
generation of patient statements, 82
Board of Directors, 58
Boutique practice, 127–129
Business of medicine, 1–2

C

CAM (complementary and alternative medicine), 136
Canceled appointments, 30, 31
   for faculty practices, 67–68
   financial impact of, 32, 36
   management of, 35–36
Cash drawer, 90–92
Cash flow problems, 111–124
   action plan for, 118–122
      action grid for consultant team, 119, 120f
      action grid for staff accountant, 119, 121f
      meetings for discussion of, 119–122
      objectives of, 119, 122–123
      results of, 122–123
   data collection for analysis of, 112–115
      expense control, 114–115, 114t
      revenue cycle, 112–114, 113f, 114t
   diagnosis of, 117
   due to too-fast growth, 111–112
   due to weak infrastructure, 115–117
      organizational chart and decision making, 116–117, 170
      staffing levels, 115–116, 116t
   immediate interventions for, 117
   strategic planning for prevention of, 123–124, 171
   turnaround strategies for, 118
      interim leadership team, 118
CBO (centralized business office), 63
Centralization, task-related, 18, 21
Centralized administration services, for outpatient academic practices, 63–64
Centralized business office (CBO), 63
Certified Medical Manager, 123
Certified medical practice executive (CMPE), 54
Character traits of employees, 96–97
Charge tickets, 9, 26, 79–80
   annual review of, 79
   auditing of, 18
   automated charge reporting, 80
   coding for, 79–80
   completing in real-time, 80
Chart audits, 18, 46, 82–83
   errors detected during, 83
   process for, 82–83

Chart documentation, computerized, 24–25
Check-in process. *See* Patient check-in
Check-writing system, 91
Checkout process. *See* Patient check-out
Claims submission, 81–82
    cash flow problems related to, 113–114
Clinical flow, 25–26, 37. *See also* Workflow problems
Clinical Telephone Tracking: Incoming Calls, 150
CMPE (certified medical practice executive), 54
Co-pays, 82
Coaching, 105–106
Coding, 79–80
    accuracy of, 80
    certification for, 105
    examining patterns of, 84, 84f
Coding expert, 80
Collections. *See also* Accounts receivable management
    of aging accounts, 89–90
    cash flow problems related to, 113–114
    of over-the-counter payments, 18, 19, 21, 86–88, 88t
Communication. *See also* Telephone calls
    e-mail, 69
    with employees, 101–103, 117
    via instant messaging, 9–10, 70
    via memos, 103
    with patients, 43–45
    between receptionist and doctors/nurses, 8–10
    between receptionist and patients, 7–11
    in staff meetings, 102–103
Communication Matrix, 45, 156
Compensation of employees, 4, 106–107
    overtime, 30, 33, 38
    reduction of, 117
Complementary and alternative medicine (CAM), 136
Computerized practice management systems
    nurses' use of, 24–25
    tracking capabilities of, 49, 50
Concierge-type practice, 125, 127–129
Confidentiality, 48
Contract disallowances, 113, 113f
Contracts, 75–78
Cosmetic surgery, 129–133, 132t, 133f

CPT codes, 79–80, 84, 86
  Payer Performance Table: Reimbursement per CPT Code, 164
Criticism of employees, 103

D

Data collection and analysis, 4
  for cash flow problems, 112–115, 113f, 114t
  for scheduling problems, 29–31
  for workflow problems, 15–16
Decision making, 4, 15
  organizational chart for, 116–117, 170
  risk management and, 41
Delegation of tasks, 23–24, 153
Diagnostic studies, 17, 18, 19, 25, 42
  "telephone in" service for results of, 50
  tracking of, 49, 157
Discharging patients, 46, 50–51, 158
Documentation, 45–48
  forms for, 46
  of incoming telephone calls, 47, 150
  of patient visits, 47–48
  for risk management, 45, 46
  standards for, 47–48
Double-booking, 30, 31, 36
Dunning messages, 89

E

E-mail, 69
E-scribing, 70
Education costs of employees, 104
EHRs (electronic health records), 24, 47, 49, 59, 70, 143, 144
Elderly patients, 9
Electronic charge reporting, 80
Electronic health records (EHRs)/electronic medical records (EMRs), 24, 47,
    49, 59, 70, 143, 144
E&M (evaluation and management) services, 83, 84, 84f
Embezzlement, 6, 90–92
  communicating consequences of, 92
  financial safeguards against, 91–92
  locations for, 91
  office practices associated with, 90–91
Employees, 95–109

absenteeism of, 60
with bad attitudes, 7–8, 108
believing in ability of, 97–98
benefits for, 104–105, 142
character traits of, 96–97
coaching of, 105–106
communication with, 101–103, 117
contributing to education costs of, 104
cost of replacing, 27
criticism of, 103
delegating tasks to, 23–24, 153
dependence on, 4
developing relationships with, 103
embezzlement by, 6, 90–92
events for recognition of, 59
exit interviews with, 108–109
as first customers, 108–109
flexibility of, 96
focus on, 142–143
insurance bonds for, 92
integrating new employees into practice, 98–100, 165
job descriptions for, 69, 116, 148
job sharing by, 104
letting go of, 107
listening to, 4, 101
morning huddles of, 8–9, 20, 21
motivation of, 2
new generations of, 142
obtaining peak performance from, 6
one-on-one meetings with, 103
opportunities taken by, 96
of outpatient academic practices, 68–69
part-time, 104
participation in professional organizations by, 105
patient advocate, 45
physicians as, 143
problem, 95, 97, 107–108
receptionist, 7–11, 148
recognizing value of, 4, 97–98, 142
recruitment of, 95, 98
reference checks for, 92
staff meetings with, 102–103, 117, 122
staffing levels for, 115–116, 116t

surveys of, 109, 167–168
team approach of, 53–60
termination of, 108
training of, 4 (*See also* Training)
turnover of, 60
visible manager of, 100–101
wages of, 4, 106–107
 overtime, 30, 33, 38
 reduction of, 117
workshops and seminars for, 104–105
EMRs (electronic medical records), 24, 47, 49, 59, 70, 143
EOB (explanation of benefits), 83, 88–89
Evaluation and management (E&M) services, 83, 84, 84f
Exam rooms
 encounters with patients in, 43–44
 optimizing clinical flow through, 25–26, 37
 patient waiting time before rooming, 30
 Rooming Matrix, 37, 155
 time to physician arrival in, 17
Exercise programs, 136
Exit interviews, 108–109
Expense control, 114–115, 114t
Explanation of benefits (EOB), 83, 88–89

F
Faculty practices. *See* Outpatient academic practices
Financial analysis, 112–115, 113f, 114t
Financial-recovery plan, 118–122
 action grid for consultant team, 119, 120f
 action grid for staff accountant, 119, 121f
 meetings for discussion of, 119–122
 objectives of, 119, 122–123
 results of, 122–123
Financial reports, 112
Financial-role diversity, 91–92
Financial safeguards, 91–92
Firing employees, 108
Flexibility of employees, 96
Future of medical practice, 4, 6, 139–145
 focus on employees, 142–143
 quality measures for, 139–141
 technology and, 143–144

G

Gastric bypass surgery, 134–136
Growth of practice, 3, 6, 60
Guidelines for Strategic Planning, 171

H

Hand-held computers, 70
Health and fitness programs, 136
HealthGrades, 139, 141
HIPAA, 46
Holistic practice, 136
Honesty, 96
Human resources (HR) management, 95–109. *See also* Employees

I

ICD-9 codes, 79–80
Information management, 142–143
Informed consent forms, 46
Infrastructure, 3, 115–117
Instant messaging, 9–10, 70
Insurance bonds for employees, 92
Insurance companies
    contracting with, 75–77
    obtaining authorization from, 18, 19
    poor-performing payers, 84–86, 164
        elimination of, 86
        hassle factor, 85
        outstanding claims reports, 85–86
        reimbursement rates, 86
    quality assurance programs of, 140
Insurance coverage
    informing patients of services not covered by, 9
    underinsured/uninsured patients, 3
Integrating new employees into practice, 98–100, 165
Internet, 70, 141

J

Job coaching, 105–106
Job descriptions, 69, 116
    for receptionist, 148
Job enrichment, 4, 105
Job sharing, 104

L

Leadership, 4, 5, 55, 109, 161
Listening to staff, 4, 101

M

Malpractice claims, 3, 41, 42
Malpractice insurance, 41, 115
Managed care organizations (MCOs), 75–76
    poor-performing payers, 84–86, 164
        elimination of, 86
        hassle factor, 85
        outstanding claims reports, 85–86
        reimbursement rates, 86
Management business office (MBO), 63
Management Information Systems (MIS), 143
Management service organization (MSO), 63
Management Skills Audit: Self-Examination of Management Behavior and
        Skills, 169
MBO (management business office), 63
MCOs. *See* Managed care organizations
MDVIP, 127–129
Medical Group Management Association (MGMA), 27t, 54, 55, 77, 84, 105,
        112, 113, 114t, 116t
Medical records. *See also* Documentation
    audits of, 46
    electronic, 24, 47, 49, 59, 70, 143, 144
    filing reports before physician's review in, 42
    patients' rights related to, 48
    respect for, 47
Medicare patients, 84, 88
Meeting Action Matrix, 166
Meetings
    to discuss cash flow problems, 119–122
    morning huddles, 8–9, 20, 21
    one-on-one, 103
    staff, 102–103, 117, 122
MGMA (Medical Group Management Association), 27t, 54, 55, 77, 84, 105,
        112, 113, 114t, 116t
MIS (Management Information Systems), 143
Missed appointments, 30, 31, 34
    for faculty practices, 67–68
    financial impact of, 32, 36
    management of, 35–36

Mission and vision statement, 55, 57, 58
Mission retreat, 55–57, 159–160
Morning huddles, 8–9, 20, 21
MSO (management service organization), 63

N

National Association of Healthcare Quality, 105
National Committee for Quality Assurance (NCQA), 140
Negligence, 47
No-shows, 30, 31, 34
    for faculty practices, 67–68
    financial impact of, 32, 36
    management of, 35–36
Non-English–speaking patients, 9
Nurse practitioners, 23, 26, 30
Nurses
    auditing of charge tickets by, 18
    computerized chart documentation by, 24–25
    nurse educator for bariatric practice, 135–136
    optimization of physician productivity by, 25–26
    paperwork handled by, 14
    patient visit time study by, 16, 151
    receptionist communication with, 8–10
    removing clerical duties from, 19
    telephone calls handled by, 14
        for obtaining insurance authorization, 18, 19
        for scheduling diagnostic studies, 18, 19
        from workers' compensation insurance adjusters, 18
    training of schedulers by, 36
Nutrition programs, 136

O

One-on-one meetings with employees, 103
Operating expenses, 114–115, 114t
Organizational chart, 116, 170
OTC payments. *See* Over-the-counter payments
Outpatient academic practices, 6, 61–74
    access to, 65–68
        missed appointments, 67–68
        optimizing clinical sessions, 67–68
        productivity and managing scheduling system, 66–67
        waiting time for appointments, 65

administrative challenges of, 62–64
    administrative secretaries, 63
    centralization, 63–64
assessing clinic performance for, 65–72
    actions based on, 73
building trust in, 72
change process in, 72–73
competing priorities of, 61
customer service of, 70–72
    commitment to, 71–72
    dispute resolution and, 71
    surveys of, 71
difference from private practices, 61–62
operational assessment of, 64–65
organizational objectives of, 64–65
patient-focused standards for, 69
staffing of, 68–69
use of technology in, 69–70
Outstanding claims reports, 85–86
Over-the-counter (OTC) payments, 18, 19, 21, 86–88
    collection goals for, 87, 88t
    policies and procedures for collection of, 87
Overtime wages, 30, 33, 38

P
PAHCOM (Professional Association of Health Care Office Management), 77, 105, 123
Partnership agreements, 122, 124
Patient advocate, 45
Patient check-in
    patient arrival time for, 17
    receptionist's responsibilities for, 7–11, 13–14
    time required for, 10, 11, 13, 17
Patient check-out, 9
    bottleneck at, 13, 14
    collecting over-the-counter payments at, 18, 19, 21, 86–88, 88t
    time required for, 18
Patient education center, 37
Patient satisfaction, 60
    with outpatient academic practices, 70
    quality of care and, 140–141
    with scheduling system, 38
    workflow problems affecting, 13, 14

Patient Satisfaction Survey, 172
Patient statements, 82, 87, 89
Patient visit time study, 16–18
Patient Visit Time Study form, 151
Patients
    abandonment of, 51
    communication with, 44–45
    discharging of, 46, 50–52, 158
    documenting visits of, 47–48
    double-booking of, 30, 31, 36
    elderly, 9
    first encounter with, 43–44
    missed appointments by, 30, 31, 34
        for faculty practices, 67–68
        financial impact of, 32, 36
        management of, 35–36
    new
        receptionist's average time with, 10
        scheduling appointments for, 17–19
        time in office, 26
    non-English–speaking, 9
    noncompliant, 46, 50
    number managed by primary care physician, 127
    physician's relationship with, 43–45
    provider time spent with, 31–32, 32f, 34, 34t
    receptionist's interactions with, 7–11
    registration of, 78–79, 79t
    research for physician selection by, 141
    responding to telephone calls of, 47
    rights of, 48
    rooming of, 17, 30, 37, 47, 155
    safety of, 139
Pay rates for employees, 106–107. *See also* Compensation of employees
Payer Performance Table: Reimbursement per CPT Code, 164
Performance monitoring, 82–88
    chart audits, 82–83
    coding patterns, 84, 84f
    identifying poor-performing payers, 84–86, 164
    office collections, 18, 19, 21, 86–88, 88t
Performance standards, 4, 47–49
    for documenting patient visits, 47–48
    monitoring compliance with, 48

patients' rights and, 48

punitive measures for noncompliance with, 48

for responding to telephone calls, 47

for rooming a patient, 47

staff training guides for, 48–49

Performance Standards Worksheet, 163

Physician-patient relationship, 43–45

Physician Quality Report, 141

Physicians

academic, 61–74

arrival in exam room after scheduled appointment time, 17

behind schedule, 29–30

delegation by, 23–24, 153

as employees, 143

examining coding patterns of, 84, 84f

individual receptionists for, 13

meetings to discuss financial-recovery plan with, 121–122

mission retreat for, 55–57, 159–160

optimizing productivity of, 23–28

partnership agreements with, 122, 124

patient research in selection of, 141

primary care

changing to boutique practice, 127–129

number of patients managed by, 127

quality of care by, 2, 5, 139–141

questionnaires of, 56, 159–160

receptionist's communication with, 8–10

revenue management responsibility of, 90

team building with, 53–60

temporary salary reductions for, 122

time out of the office of, 31, 33, 33t

tracking time spent with patients, 31–32, 32f

use of hand-held computers by, 70

working in real-time, 27, 29

Physician's Retreat Questionnaire, 159–160

Plastic reconstructive surgeons, shifting to cosmetics, 129–133, 132t, 133f

Pre-collection letter-writing services, 89

Pre-employment physical exams, 31, 32f

Problem employees, 95, 97, 107–108

Problem solving, 97

Productivity, 2, 23–28

clinical flow and, 25–26

delegation and, 23–24, 153
missed appointments and, 31
performance measures of, 27, 27t
physician time out of the office and, 31, 33, 33t
scheduling system for optimization of, 38
    in outpatient academic practices, 66–67
team approach to patient care and, 26–27
technology and, 24, 25
workflow model for improvement of, 21
Professional Association of Health Care Office Management (PAHCOM),
    77, 105, 123
Professional organizations, 105

Q
Quality, 2, 5, 139–141
    of business practices, 141
    improvement initiatives for, 140
    monitoring within medical office, 141
    patient safety and, 139
    patient satisfaction and, 140–141
    performance measures of, 140, 141
Quality Plus standards, 140

R
Reception area
    patient waiting time in, 10, 30
    patients too ill to be comfortable in, 44
    tidying of, 10
Receptionists, 5, 7–11
    average time with new patient, 10
    check-out, 9
    daily responsibilities of, 9–11
    handling of appointment calls by, 16–17
        elimination of, 19
    importance of, 7, 8, 11
    incompetent, 8
    for individual physicians, 13
    job description for, 148
    morning huddles with, 8–9
    poor attitudes and practices of, 7–8
    productivity of, 21
    workflow problems affecting, 13–21
Reconstructive surgeons, shifting to cosmetics, 129–133, 132t, 133f

Record keeping, 45–48. *See also* Documentation
Recruitment, 95, 98
Reference checks, 92
Registration of patients, 78–79, 79t
Reimbursement for services, 3. *See also* Revenue management
  claims submission for, 81–82, 113–114
  co-pays, 82
  contracting for, 75–77
  denied, 89
  discharging patients for noncompliance with, 50, 51, 158
  patient statements for, 82, 87, 89
  poor-performing payers, 84–86
    elimination of, 86
    hassle factor, 85
    outstanding claims reports, 85–86
    reimbursement rates, 86
  third-party reimbursement analysis, 88–89, 164
Relationships with employees, 103
Relationships with patients, 43–45
Reshaping the practice, 6, 125–137
  to bariatric practice, 134–136
  to boutique practice, 127–129
  choices for, 125, 137
  commitment to, 125–127
  to cosmetic surgery practice, 129–133, 132t, 133f
  exploratory questions for, 126
  feasibility study before, 126
  other opportunities for, 136–137
  self-examination for, 125–126
Revenue cycle, 112–114, 113f, 114t
Revenue management, 6, 75–93
  accounts receivable, 88–90
  capturing charges, 75–79
    contracting, 75–77
    keeping staff informed, 77–78
    patient registration, 78–79, 79t
  charge tickets, 79–80
    coding for, 79, 80
  embezzlement, 6, 90–93
  impact of physician time out of the office, 31, 33, 33t
  monitoring performance, 82–88
    chart audits, 82–83

    coding patterns, 84, 84f
    identifying poor-performing payers, 84–86, 164
    office collections, 18, 19, 21, 86–88, 88t
  physician responsibility for, 90
  revenue-recovery standards, 81–82
  scheduling system for, 32, 38
Risk management, commonsense, 5–6, 41–52
  attitudes about, 52
  components of plan for, 45–46
  developing written plan for, 45–46
  discharging patients, 46, 50–51, 158
  documentation for, 45, 46
  elements of, 41–42
  office practices and, 42
  performance standards for, 47–48
    punitive measures for noncompliance with, 48
    staff training guides for, 48–49
  physician-patient relationship in, 43–45
  resources for, 52
  tracking systems for, 49–50
Risk/Opportunity Matrix, 65, 162
Rooming Matrix, 37, 155
Rooming patients, 17, 30, 47
Rural practice, 3

S

Safety of patients, 139
Salaries, 106–107. *See also* Compensation of employees
Sample Bio Sketch: Meet Our Newest Addition!, 165
Sample Discharge Letter, 158
Sample Job Description: Receptionist, 148
Sample Organizational Chart, 170
Schedulers, 18, 19
  training of, 36
Scheduling, 29–39. *See also* Appointments
  financial impact of unmanaged system for, 32–33, 33t
  gains from revised system of, 38–39
  objectives of system for, 33–34
  open-access system for, 36
  problems with, 29–30
    analysis of, 30–32
  system for outpatient academic practices, 66–67

template for, 34–35, 34t
   implementation of, 37
   monitoring results of, 38
   preparing for implementation of, 35–37
   staff support for, 35, 38–39
Seminars for employees, 104–105
Society of Medical-Dental Management Consultants/National Association of
       Healthcare Consultants (SMD/NAHC), 27t, 55, 112, 113, 114t,
       116t
Sports medicine, 136
Staff. *See* Employees; Nurses; Physicians
Staff meetings, 102–103, 117, 122
Staff Survey: How Does Management Rate?, 167–168
Staffing levels, 115–116, 116t
Standards. *See* Performance standards
State of Health Care Quality, The, 140
Strategic planning, 123–124, 171

T
Task-related centralization, 18, 21
Team approach to patient care, 25–26
Team building, 53–60
   leadership for, 55, 161
   mission retreat for, 55–57, 159–160
   physician interviews and questionnaires for, 55, 159–160
   power of team, 59–60
   sharing goals for, 59
   strengthening the team, 57–59
   team spirit for, 59
   team thinking for, 55
Team Leader Tips, 161
Technology, 4, 24, 143–144
   electronic medical records, 24, 47, 49, 59, 70, 143, 144
   for information management, 142–143
   in outpatient academic practices, 69–70
Telephone Appointment Tracking, 149
Telephone calls, 9, 15–20
   abandoned, 14, 15
   for appointments, 16–20
      hours of, 17
      number of schedulers required for, 18
      time required for, 16–17

volume of, 16–17
Clinical Telephone Tracking: Incoming Calls form, 150
documentation of, 47
dropping to voice mail, 14, 15, 16–17
lunchtime coverage for, 19
monitoring number and length of, 20
nurses' handling of, 14
to obtain insurance authorization, 18, 19
for payment, 89
peak times for, 16
standards for handling of, 47, 48
Telephone Appointment Tracking form, 149
"telephone in" service for test results, 50
from workers' compensation insurance adjusters, 18
"Telephone medicine," 32
Terminating employees, 108
Thinking "out of the box," 4
Third-party payers
contracting with, 75–77
poor-performing payers, 84–86
elimination of, 86
hassle factor, 85
outstanding claims reports, 85–86
reimbursement rates, 86
reimbursement analysis of, 88–89, 164
report of aging accounts, 89–90
Tickler files, 49–50
Time analysis
checkout time, 18
completion of in-house diagnostic studies, 17
impact of physician time out of the office, 31, 33, 33t
patient time in reception area, 10, 30
patient visit time study, 16–18, 151
patients' rooming time, 17
physician arrival in room after appointment time, 17
provider time spent with patients, 31–32, 32f, 34, 34t
receptionist time with new patient, 10
scheduling outside diagnostic studies, 17, 18
telephone calls for appointments, 16–17
Toolbox forms, 6, 147–172
Appointment Power Words Matrix: a Guide to Managing Appointments, 154
The Art of Delegation, 153

Clinical Telephone Tracking: Incoming Calls, 150
Communication Matrix, 156
Guidelines for Strategic Planning, 171
Management Skills Audit: Self-Examination of Management Behavior and
    Skills, 169
Meeting Action Matrix, 166
Patient Satisfaction Survey, 172
Patient Visit Time Study, 151
Payer Performance Table: Reimbursement per CPT Code, 164
Performance Standards Worksheet, 163
Physician's Retreat Questionnaire, 159–160
Risk/Opportunity Matrix, 162
Rooming Matrix, 155
Sample Bio Sketch: Meet Our Newest Addition!, 165
Sample Discharge Letter, 158
Sample Job Description: Receptionist, 148
Sample Organizational Chart, 170
Staff Survey: How Does Management Rate?, 167–168
Team Leader Tips, 161
Telephone Appointment Tracking, 149
Tracking Log: Diagnostic Studies, 157
Training Monitor, 152
Tracking Log: Diagnostic Studies, 157
Tracking systems, 49–50
Training, 4
    to alleviate workflow problems, 18
    for patient registration, 78–79, 79t
    on record keeping, 45
    for risk management, 46, 48–49
    of schedulers, 36
Training Monitor form, 152
Transworld Systems, 89
Travel medicine, 136
Turnover of employees, 60

U

Uninsured/underinsured patients, 3
Urban practice, 3

V

Voice mail (VM), 14, 15, 16–17

W

Wages for employees, 4, 106–107
   overtime, 30, 33, 38
   reduction of, 117
Weight reduction programs, 136
Wellness programs, 136
Work-ins, 30, 31, 32
Workers' compensation cases, 18, 19
Workflow problems, 6, 13–22
   challenge of, 14–15
   collecting data on, 15–16
   examples of, 13–14
   peak times for, 17
   solutions for, 18–19
      gaining physician support for, 19–20
      implementation of, 20–21
   systems for, 15
   time analysis for, 16–18
Working in real-time, 27, 29, 80
Workshops for employees, 104–105